THE CHAIN OF

THE
CHAIN OF LIFE

by
Dr GUYON RICHARDS

THE C.W. DANIEL COMPANY LTD.
1 Church Path, Saffron Walden
Essex, England

Second Edition 1954
Second Impression February 1974
Third Impression 1982

ISBN 0 85032 119 0

Printed in Great Britain by
The Eastern Press Ltd.
of London and Reading

DEDICATED
TO
MY WIFE
AND OUR
FOUR SONS

PREFACE

I STARTED to write a book to describe results of research obtained by using a modification of the Abrams' method. It has grown into something more than this. I trust it will interest some outside the medical profession, for the more we know about ourselves the better. The type that fears knowledge is dying out. The best hope I have is that it may stimulate some younger and abler man to take up the same line of research. I have tried to acknowledge debts in the text. My thanks are due to Mr. E. L. Grant Watson for much painstaking work reading my chapters and giving me excellent advice which I have not always followed, but he has helped me a lot in making me rewrite a number of chapters till they were intelligible. I have to thank Lt.-Col. H. T. T. Lefroy, R.E., Rtd., and Dr. Kenneth Sandeman, for technical advice. I have gratefully to acknowledge the loyal help I have had from my subject and secretary, Mr. David Smith—without his zeal and sensitivity to impressions I could not possibly have got through the work. I have had help from my sons in designing the circuit, especially from Gerald, who designed and made the valve unit. I have to gratefully acknowledge the help of Mr. T. Loveday in revision of the book as a whole from a literary point of view and for wise suggestions.

I have to thank the following for subscriptions to a research fund : Mr. Howard Back, Mr. J. E. Watts Carlton, Sir James Barr, Dr. Mather Thomson, Dr. Oscar Parkes, Dr. Dodson Hessey, Dr. J. Kempster, Dr. Muirhead Martin.

W. GUYON RICHARDS.

At Lord Lister's House,
Park Crescent,
London.

CONTENTS

CHAPTER		PART I.			PAGE
I.	WIRELESS IN NATURE	..	..	..	1
II.	ABRAMS' DISCOVERIES	..	..	..	6
III.	THE TESTING CIRCUIT	..	..	..	10
IV.	THE ATOM AND THE OHM	..	..	..	20
V.	THE ATOMIC TABLE	..	..	..	26
VI.	MORE ABOUT THE ATOM	..	..	..	32
VII.	POLARITY	..	..	..	35
VIII.	BALANCE	..	..	..	41
IX.	SECONDARY TUNING	..	..	..	45

PART II.

X.	ANATOMICAL STUDY	..	..	..	47
XI.	INTERNAL SECRETIONS	..	..	..	51
XII.	BIOMORPHS AND AURA	..	..	..	84

PART III.

XIII.	RECOGNITION OF CONDITIONS	..	..	107
XIV.	STAGES IN DISEASE	..	..	113
XV.	INFLAMMATORY DISEASE	..	..	119
XVI.	TREATMENT	..	..	..	129
XVII.	CANCER	..	..	..	155
XVIII.	DIETING	..	..	..	179
XIX.	COLOUR	..	..	..	189
XX.	THE OSCILLOCLAST	..	..	..	196
XXI.	THOUGHT FORMS (THEIR EFFECT ON THE TESTING CIRCUIT)	..	..	201
XXII.	THE FUTURE	..	..	..	210
	INDEX	..	..	..	214

INTRODUCTION

ONE of the things I am frequently asked is " How did you come to take up this work ? " I usually relate how certain happenings led me to study Abrams' work. On reflection I see that meeting people and being told certain facts do not make a man go in for pioneering along lines which cannot be called popular. To do this there must. be some kind of psychological make-up. As a lad at school and Cambridge I was very happy and conservative ; the world was an excellent place, full of good fellows and charming girls. During my time at Bart.'s I went through a stage of religious revolt. My first attempt at reform was joining in an effort to amalgamate the Sports Clubs. This led to my being made Secretary of the amalgamation. My next effort was when I was selected as personal assistant by Surgeon-General W. R. Browne ; together we put down the system of corruption which prevailed in the Madras Civil Medical Department and reformed the Records Department. Corruption in India is a matter of immemorial custom. The match was played on both sides without rancour. My chief opponent was a gentleman and a man of kindly humour and great ability.

This effort caused Surgeon-General Bomford, Director-General of the Indian Medical Service, to ask me to take a post in Medical Supply. Again there was a conflict. I succeeded in carrying out certain reforms, but the powers above then wearied and I was presently returned to surgical life in the district of Salem, to my great satisfaction.

Life in an Indian district means acting for oneself. The Salem district was a hundred miles long by eighty broad ; in this area I was the last word in surgery and medicine. In sanitation I had to meet entirely fresh problems, for instance the guinea worm, hitherto untackled. To secure successful action I had to persuade a dozen or more divisional and municipal authorities to work with me and not against me.

Acting for oneself means thinking for oneself. Medical and sanitation problems in India vary in different districts ; if one does not learn self-reliance in such a life one is rather less than a man.

As there is so much to do, in which the old authorities at home would be as much at sea as a newly-joined subaltern, your old attitude of reverence wears thinner and you learn to think in all matters for yourself. I can think of no better training of the spirit and mind for a man who is to do pioneer work. Often it is a matter of making do with inadequate tools.

Life in the Indian service also has a broadening effect on mind and spirit. No man can live the formative years of his life in the East without getting his foundations altered in some degree. The class of person who regards Eastern ideas as just " native superstition " is rare in the Indian services and practically non-existent in the districts. Gross superstition and foul immorality exist, but there is also a culture far older than our own whose ideas are poles apart from our Western materialism. Side by side with poorer features there is a simple and open religious atmosphere which is refreshing after our somewhat shamefaced attitude. Only the products of our Western teaching pretend they are materialists.

I left India with an open mind, and as far as I can judge was ready to receive further experiences on any plane.

Two things alone seem to be real knowledge. Firstly, that the real personality, the Ego has been and goes on, and secondly, that we all get a square deal.

This seems to me to be definite knowledge brought from another existence, and not worth arguing about.

As to details of Religion, Science, Sociology, they are matters to be thought about and discussed. Some matters seem to be historical or scientific facts.

I have tried to add to these, and for all new work there is the test of time.

One other lesson I learnt was that work must be done for the joy of doing it—the result may remain in Other hands. I have had approval of my chiefs, and disapproval. Approval is good ; results are better.

The Great War put an end to my work in the East ; I came home sick and just escaped the Emdem who captured five of a string of six boats, we alone escaped owing to our Captain's caution.

My next phase was service in the Kitchener Hospital, Brighton, for Indian troops. I had charge of two surgical blocks, and here again the spirit of reform overcame me. I started remedial exercises for my own blocks. This was contrary to discipline, and Col. Sir Bruce Seton's sentence was that I was to form and take charge of an Orthopædic

Department. In 1915 Captain Sandes, of the I.M.S., introduced me to the benefits of ionisation and other means of electrical treatment, and when he had to return to India I had to do his work in addition to all my previous work. Again the punishment fitted the crime. Incidentally I may say that my wards were all run unconsciously on electrical lines, for all the cases that required daily dressing were treated on Sir Almroth Wright's lines with salt solution, and all cases which required rest were packed with B.I.P.P., which is a non-conductor owing to its high paraffin content. When I was invalided out of the service and started general practice I continued using electrical forms of treatment, for though ignorant I was becoming electrically-minded. This prepared my mind for my meeting with Mr. A. E. Baines, and what he had to teach me in regard to the electrical conditions of the human body.

One morning when I was so busy that I did not know how I was going to get through the work, I was told that a gentleman wanted to see me to talk about dielectric oil. Fortunately Baines came into the surgery, and one look at him decided me to hear what he had to say. I had no time to talk then, but he accepted an invitation to dinner, and during the evening he opened up for me a new view as to the nature of human mechanism. Eventually Baines came to stay in Burgess Hill and I started to study the human body and plants in health and disease with a d'Arsonval galvanometer. I cannot deal with Baines' work here. My own work lies with radiations that we may term wireless, as these will cross space without conducting wires. But Baines prepared my mind for Abrams' and Kilner's work. I found a galvanometer very useful, and Baines' simple methods of using dielectrics and electrolites in the treatment of various conditions, of great practical use. His principle was to balance the electrical condition by increasing or decreasing current as requisite, judging the condition by the action of the affected part on the galvanometer. Every household should stock standard dielectric oil : it is the best treatment for burns and scalds ; blisters should be emptied and the part covered in lint soaked in oil. In every case I have so treated there has been no shock. I have also had most excellent results in pneumonia.

Baines introduced me to Abrams' methods. When Baines first told me that Abrams could diagnose the position of a cancer from a drop of the patient's blood I replied " impossible."

However, he continued to excite my interest, and when a breakdown in health occurred from overwork I had an opportunity to study Abrams' writings and later to experience, by Dr. Mather Thompson's kindness, the benefits of treatment by the oscilloclast, otherwise known as Abrams' Box.

A. E. Baines was one of the most unselfish and devoted scientists I have ever met. His one thought was how to use the knowledge he had acquired for others' benefit. It is an honour to have been associated with him.

My breakdown in health was brought on by overwork, and as I had just arranged to send my two elder sons to Cambridge it seemed a great blow to be deprived of my means of livelihood.

However it was in the end the best thing for me. I got time to study a fresh subject and think. I also had an opportunity to realise the effect of the oscilloclast on myself and others. Within nine months of my giving up my practice I was at work again at Hastings using Abrams' methods under the guidance of Dr. Dodson Hessey. Very soon I had a fresh period of discontent, the results of which I relate in my book.

Abrams laid a very wide basis which I conceive was his job. It never occurred to him to find out what his figures meant. He has been blamed for wasting time and energy over researches on the effect of having red hair or having certain religious beliefs, or other psychological problems. Abrams worked many hours a day and these queer inquiries he regarded as play. His dæmon meant him to show that colour, thought, emotion, everything material or immaterial alike, caused vibrations in the human frame ; in this task he eminently succeeded.

I have tried to carry his work a step or two further. My dæmon seems to have a passion for practical knowledge and straightening things out.

It involves a lot of tiring work, but the work itself is fascinating and the results of definitely practical interest.

My contention is that medicine should include everything pertaining to man's nature.

The more you know about it the better. Man is body, soul and spirit, and you need to treat all three. Man's nature can be divided into more parts than three, but these are sufficient to indicate my meaning. Drugs or the knife is not enough, food and environment and emotional troubles must all be gone into. The psyche is more important than the body, but each part of man is woven into the other.

Further, we must consider man's place in the cosmos.

Who can judge of his own action and reactions ? Read the life-history of anyone who has done anything worth doing, and however much he or she has marred it in the doing you will see that the driving power has been from some power outside.

As far as one can see one's own life, there has been at intervals in mine an overpowering sense of discontent with things as they are, which is quite at variance with the happy, contented conservative I was in early youth. This has led to action in a very limited sphere in each case.

There are lots of things to be done ; nothing is too well done. Well here's luck to the rebels, for they want it. I admire them in every case, but I do not always like their methods. It is not always necessary to destroy before you build or vilify opponents who are only performing their allotted task.

A man must follow the task laid on him. He is given the physical, mental and spiritual attributes necessary for the job he has to perform.

Had Abrams had greater electrical knowledge or more knowledge of wireless he might have missed things he did find out, because he would have thought them impossible. There are endless things that would be useful to me now, but working from knowing very little of my own subject I have been able to develop my own methods free from prejudice. I do not think the less of Abrams, Hahnemann, Almroth Wright or Baines, or any man I have learnt from because I do not follow their methods entirely.

And now why did I follow in part any of them ? It appeared to me to be due to self-determination, but who knows what part the Fates take in shaping this individual life of ours— just one thread in the pattern they weave. The Fates are rightly featured as women, for do not all able ladies persuade their men that they are the masters of their actions ?

PART I

CHAPTER I

WIRELESS IN NATURE

WHEN seeking a title for this book I thought of calling it " Human Wireless," but my friend Colonel H. P. T. Lefroy, R.E., Retd., who has helped me by advice and criticism, objected to this on the grounds that my work extended beyond man and that it was customary to talk of " wireless " waves as being within certain limits, whereas the phenomena I was dealing with were probably outside these limits.

The term " wireless " is, however, too convenient to be dropped—no other single word can convey the idea of impulses crossing space. I agree that " Human Wireless " would be too limited a title, but I do not agree to limit the term wireless to a certain range of frequencies which happen to be within the compass of artificial wireless. The phenomena with which I have dealt here are spread all through Nature. There appears to me to be a universal rhythm which runs all through those parts of the cosmos which have been investigated and doubtless extends to the whole.

The solar system, and this small planet, the Earth, and Man, who prides himself on being the latest development of life upon it, are each and all in their turn manifestations of the universal substance. The elements, of which our bodies are made, are the same as in the rocks and the atmosphere, and whether in us, or in the sun, or in the depths of the earth, they obey the same chemical and physical laws. We ourselves are at one, in our bodily-functioning, with all other animate bodies, and we touch spheres where the law is difficult to comprehend, but where there are intimations that it is probably the same as that which governs the physical universe.

The etheric waves which are broadcast and received on our wireless sets are not isolated phenomena, they exist throughout the solar system. These waves which we receive on the wireless are but *one* kind of wave which travels in the ether of space. They are far larger than the waves which excite heat, and immensely larger than the minute tremors which enter the eye and, stimulating the nervous mechanism of the retina, give us the sense of sight. All these different waves in the ether travel at the same incredibly rapid speed and have, as their origin, definite causes.

What are these causes and how are waves in the ether produced ? I merely use the term ether as a convenient expression for interatomic and interstellar space. Before answering this question, even in the roughest manner, it is well to remember that all material objects and all particles are connected by the Ether. In it they move, and of it they may be composed. The particles embedded in the Ether, the electrons and the protons, are comparable to minute crystals formed in a mother-liquor, and they are minutely small in comparison with the spaces which separate them. Thus the electrons in the atom are, to their containing atom, in the same proportion as the planets are to the solar system ; and we may regard the solar system as a magnified atom, and the atom as a minutely minimised solar system. Both consist of material particles separated by comparatively vast fields of Ether.

To return now to our question. It can roughly, and by analogy, be answered by saying, that as the vibrations of a tuning fork cause waves of sound in the air, so a vibrating electron stimulates waves in the ether. Further, we know that the activity of radiation depends upon the pace of the electron round the nucleus of the atom, and this depends upon the distance of the electrons from the nucleus.

When Senator Marconi discovered a method of sending messages across space he was not creating ; man cannot create in this sense, he was merely adapting for our use in business and in pleasure what Nature was already doing. We know but little at present about this form of radiation, but there are facts which show that waves of probably very similar nature are sent out by plants, animals and men, and received often at a great distance.

The contention of this book is that radiations from the atom take place from all kinds of matter, and are always operative from all things animate and inanimate, and that it is possible, by means of a constructed mechanism, to identify the elements in living substances by these " wireless waves " which are being continually sent out, and further that the recording of such waves offers a reliable means of diagnosis in cases of disease.

Before coming to the description of this apparatus and the

account of the work which has already been accomplished, it is of interest to notice some of those cases both in animals and men where long-distance messages are constantly sent out and received. In the animal world a large portion of what has hitherto been called instinct may well be accounted for by a definite mechanism operating either in the atmosphere or in the ether.

The insect kingdom is rich in such examples. I will cite but a few.

In the early spring, towards the end of February, the Kentish Glory moth emerges from her cocoon which has lain through the winter amongst dead leaves close to the ground. By short flights or by climbing she reaches the high-growing twigs of the silver birch trees. Here, after impregnation, she lays her eggs. As yet there is no sign of a leaf, only bare twigs. In her natural state, the moth never makes a mistake as to the tree on which she lays her eggs ; were she to do so, and lay her eggs on any other kind of tree, or upon any other portion of the tree than the young twigs, the young caterpillars would not find the right sort of food to live on and, being too weak to walk far to find it, would certainly die. For their survival it is necessary for the mother moth to place her eggs in the one right place, namely, on the terminal twigs where the young leaves will be easy to find. The moth cannot know that these bare twigs are going, long after she is dead, to blossom into leaves, yet she invariably places her eggs in the right place. Is it not probable that with some receiving set of which we know nothing, she receives a message from the birch twigs announcing their rightness for her purpose, which stimulates her to the laying of eggs ?

It is well known that the male moths of certain species will assemble from great distances to find the females. The French naturalist, J. H. Fabre, carried out extensive experiments on the Great Emperor moth and the Oak Eggar. He recorded how hundreds of male moths came in course of a few nights to visit one female. Neither the Emperor moth nor the Oak Eggar were common in his locality, yet this large number of males found their way from distant places to visit the female confined in his study. They certainly received some kind of message. When the moth was confined in an air-tight box the males were not attracted, yet the message : " Female moth of my species " which the males received, was not in the nature of a scent, for no strong covering scent could obscure it and, moreover, it was found to travel up-wind and not down-wind, as would be the case of an air-borne

RADIANT ENERGY WAVE CHART

SUNLIGHT ENERGY DIAGRAM

Infinity ←

	Ultra-Violet	Visible (Luminous Spectrum)	Infra Red	Till recently an Unknown Region	Electric Waves	Hertzian Waves	Wireless Waves	→ Infinity
	Invisible Actinic Rays / Ionising Rays		Invisible Heat Rays	Rays yielding to Recent Research	Waves detected by the Coherer etc.	Waves discovered by Hertz His experiments ranged about the wave length of 60 cm.	Now utilised in Radio Engineering	
OCTAVES	1	2 3	4 5 6 7 8 9 10 11	12 13 14 15	16 17	11 OCTAVES }	11 OCTAVES	
WAVE LENGTHS	0·1µ	1µ	10µ / 100µ	1mm	1cm	5 to 10 METERS	10 to 20000 METERS	
VIBRATIONS PER SECOND	1,600 million million	800 million million	400 to 100 million million	300,000 to 30,000 million	30,000 million	6 million to 30 million	30 million to 15 thousand	

Rays:- that never reach us from the sun
They are absorbed in the higher layers of the atmosphere
(Heaviside Layer) Producers

Cosmic Rays
Wave length of 2AU or less
Wave length of 10 very hardest Gamma rays is wave length of shortest cosmic rays

AU = Angstrōm unit = one millionth of a millimeter
µ = micron = one thousandth of a millimeter

X and Gamma Rays Wave lengths of 2AU or less

KNOWN WAVE-LENGTHS IN MILLIMETRES

X and Gamma Rays	·00001 about.	
Schumann Waves	·00010	
Ultra-Violet	·00020 to ·00035 } 2 to 4 Octaves.	
Extreme Violet	·00040	
Blue	·00045	
Green	·00050 } 1 Octave.	
Yellow	·00058	
Red	·00085	
Extreme Red	·00072	
Residual Rays	·0085 to 096 } 9 or 10 Octaves.	
Infra Red 1µ	·001 to 0·1	

scent. How this message is conveyed no one yet knows, we only know that it exists. Might it not well be an etheric wave, but of such a nature that it cannot penetrate a shield of material substance ?

Many instances of telepathy have been well established, and I need not record them here. We realise that those who live together in amity send and pick up mental images very frequently. We know that the action of crowds is influenced by such waves. Fear spreads faster than any visible thing ; emotions in a large number of minds acting together are immensely powerful, and will generate fear, courage, hysteria or a feeling of reverence. These are all cases of waves passing through space. There are, doubtless, an enormous number of different kinds. In my work I have been attempting to find out something about those waves which are given off by the human body and which, in my opinion, correspond to all the multiplicity of the compounds which it combines.

During the year 1929, while working for the Bell Telephone Laboratory in America, Englund found that his own body interfered with experiments when he was working with waves below four metres in length, and he eventually came to the conclusion that his own body was giving off waves of 3·66 metres. A parallel case occurred some years ago when A. E. Baines was sent to investigate errors in the work of testing submarine cables in South Africa. He found that the observer's own current caused errors which varied during the day ; they were larger when the operator was rested and fresh, and less after some hours of work, and they could be minimised by earthing the body while testing. Such currents can be measured on a galvanometer. The waves which we are discussing have not yet been measured with certainty, but for some years past there has been a growing tendency among certain physicians to regard these waves, in their varying intensities, as reliable indicators of health and disease.

CHAPTER II

ABRAMS' DISCOVERIES

DR. ALBERT ABRAMS of San Francisco was one of the first physicians to turn his attention towards these wireless waves which emanate from the human body. In the same indirect manner as Röntgen, who first obtained his X-ray effect whilst working at a different problem, so Abrams became aware of the electro-magnetic waves of the human body whilst studying the spinal reflexes by means of percussion. It was by chance that he found that all tubercular patients gave a dull sound when tapped at certain spots on their backs, and that this dullness was present in all cases of tuberculosis, whether there was lung disease in that situation or not. He further found that he only obtained this dull sound when the patient was facing west, and that it disappeared when he turned the patient so as to face north and south. This fact suggested that there was a relation between the electro-magnetic field of the earth and that of the individual. He further found that if he held a tubercular specimen, either a piece of tissue or a tube containing tubercle bacilli, over the back of the neck of a healthy person, the same dullness was present on percussion. This experiment certainly suggested that wireless waves from the specimen were received and recorded by the body, and that these waves altered the character of the healthy tissues. His next experiment was to pass a wire from a patient to a healthy person, one end of the wire being over the lesion on the patient and the other being on the cervical vertebra. He next found that on tapping the back and abdomen of the healthy person he obtained the same dullness as when tapping the diseased patient. This may be regarded as an amplification of the earlier experiment, and goes to show that waves from the diseased patient passed along the wire, altering temporarily the electro-magnetic condition of the tissues of the healthy, who was termed the subject. At about this time Dr. Abrams made another discovery. He was percussing a patient, and found on the abdomen a dullness for which he could not account ; he then noticed that there was a bottle containing a cancer growth on his table. He had it removed, and the dullness disappeared. The growth was brought back, and the dullness reappeared. He had thus found two separate reflexes on different areas, one for tubercle and another for cancer. This was surely an astonishing observation, and formed the basis of his future work. Experiments were repeated again and again, and each one gave fresh evidence of the passage of waves across space.

Experiments followed with other diseases. He found that syphilis caused a reflex on much the same area as cancer. So area-reflex was not enough in itself ; further evidence was needed for differentiation. A measure of wave-length was what was required. The plan he adopted was to interpose a coiled wire resistance between the patient or the specimen and the subject. He had a coil wound with resistances in ohms marked on it. He then found that diseases came through on the human indicator or subject at certain points on the coil. He also found that the best place for the reception of the waves from the patient was the forehead of the subject, when he was using the abdominal muscles of the subject as his indicator. The abdominal muscles of a human being are peculiarly sensitive to the electro-magnetic condition of the organs and of the body generally, and as a banjo string can be stimulated to vibrate to waves of sound, so these muscles can be stimulated to reflex movements by changes in the electro-magnetic field. When following this method of diagnosis through percussion, Abrams found that in cases of malaria, dullness occurred with his rheostat set at 32 ohms, with tubercle at 42 ; with an infection due to *Bacillus coli* at 44 ; with acquired syphilis at 55 ; with hereditary syphilis at 57 ; with cancer at 50 ; with sarcoma at 58 ; with a streptococcal infection at 60. He spent a long time working out various disease conditions, and his next step was to find remedies. He naturally tried the well-known drugs first, and also coloured lights and pigments. He found that quinine gave a reaction when the rheostat was set at a resistance of 32 ohms. Having spent some time at this work on the reaction obtained from drugs, he was not satisfied with the results, so tried to construct a machine which would give the waves that he wanted. Various trials led to the manufacture of the oscilloclast, or wave-breaker, commonly known as Abrams' box.

From what has already been said it is clear that the two great discoveries made by Dr. Abrams are as follows :—

One.—That all matter is radio-active, and that the waves generated by this activity can be picked up across space by using the human reflexes as a detector.

Two.—That in certain diseases, dull patches are found in the patient which constantly occurred when those particular diseases were present.

It is one of the unkind blows of fate that for some years Abrams has been known chiefly as the inventor of the oscilloclast. This instrument is of very little importance compared with the above-mentioned discoveries. It is an irony that his general reputation should be valued or decried on the merits or demerits of a bit of mechanism, and that his real contribution to our knowledge should be so much ignored. The oscilloclast has been a useful instrument, but Abrams' teaching would have spread more quickly had he never invented it, for it has obscured from the profession and the public the larger issues. The apparatus which Abrams used for the diagnosis of disease consisted, in its simplest form, of a round black wooden box containing metallic contact points from which ran grounding wires. From the metallic top of this box passes a short insulated wire to a specialised type of rheostat, capable of measuring up to 61 ohms. From this rheostat passes another insulating wire, having on its free end an aluminium electrode which is applied to the forehead of the subject. This apparatus has been modified and improved upon, but the above description is sufficient to show his system working at its simplest. His method of using the apparatus was as follows : A specimen of the patient's blood was placed in the box and experimental percussions made on the abdomen of the subject, the indicator being moved at each tapping from one ohm upwards. When a dullness of sound was perceived, the reading on the rheostat was marked. And thus, from previous experiments and readings taken from diseased tissues, he considered the disease was identified.

The oscilloclast, Abrams' device for destroying infections and malignancies through the application of measured vibrations, operated from a battery or from the main, and delivered the proper electronic destructive vibration to suit the condition. His theory was that the vibrations broke down the disease in the patient. It was probably wrong, but he obtained good results. Waves from the oscilloclast will not kill microorganisms ; if they give relief it is by stimulation of the patient's cells and the production of a protective substance.

I have had to devise new methods of diagnosis as Abrams' original figures proved inadequate, being based on the changes of a single atom in each case.

Abrams' task was, I conceive, to prove the radio-activity of all matter and to give us a method by which diagnosis could be made more accurate, and the nature of man in health and disease studied.

His book " New Conceptions," covers a very wide field ; he touches on all sorts of themes ; it is difficult to follow ; it reads like the notes of a very busy man who has not had time to arrange his ideas, but if you study it carefully you find that he is working various methods to show the activity across space of life-force in various forms.

He shows that male energy differs in its effects from female energy as indicated by the waves coming off the fingers of the right or left hand. He measures energy in various ways, and finds that, by concentrating, a poet could give off greater energy than an athlete.

He studies the effect of thought on religion, or on sex, of colour in the hair ; his researches cover an immensely wide area and he was untiring in work. It is said that he worked fourteen hours a day. He devised a method by which he thought he could tell how long every life's energy would last and foretold, it is said, his own span. When his last illness came he refused to stop working, " There is so much to do, and time is short," he said.

Whatever we may think of Abrams' work all must admire his unflagging enthusiasm and his ardent search for truth.

He was a very wealthy man, but he chose to spend laborious days working in his laboratory and consulting room till he dropped exhausted by his labours. Abrams never paused to answer his critics. He was not a man to put up with heckling. He had his work to do and was burnt up with the passion for research. " Come and learn if you like, or stay away," was his attitude.

The chief principles of his teaching will live in one form or another, although the world in general may be slow to recognise them. The men who now base their work on his discoveries should pay homage to the untiring enthusiast who discovered human wireless and who was able to record by its means the alterations in balance which accompany diseased conditions.

CHAPTER III

THE CIRCUIT

SOME of my older readers will remember the late Alfred Capper, the "Thought Reader." Capper, as he explained, did not read "thoughts," but the effect of thought on the nerve muscle apparatus of those who took part in his experiments. One of the items in his entertainments was to direct some of those who went on to the platform to think of a pain. Capper held the hand of the person who was concentrating on an idea, and in a few seconds announced where the pain was seated. When concentration was good Capper always succeeded in a correct diagnosis. Certain sensitives can localise a lesion by contact without the patients' active co-operation. It was this power of living tissue acting on the consciousness of another when adequate contact is made that Abrams made use of in his circuit. The electrical forces and tensions of the human body had been studied and measured by means of various kinds of galvanometer and valuable knowledge obtained. The genius of Abrams directed him to combine physical measurement with the sensitiveness of life for living forces.

Abrams' original testing set was very simple ; it consisted of an electrode place on the patient connected by a wire to a measuring rheostat, a wire from this was attached to the forehead of the living indicator or subject. The reflexes of the abdominal muscles of this subject were elicited by percussion by the observer. Later he completed the circuit by grounding the patient and subject. The essential life-factor is not the subject but the observer. The subject can be replaced by a bakelite plate which is stroked by the observer's fingers. He then elicits his own reactions. This modification is a great loss, because the subject's body becomes in the circuit a sympathetic living map of the patient's body, even when the patient is represented by merely a few drops of blood or serum. The reason for this is by no means apparent but I apprehend it is connected with a law which might be stated thus : "Every part of the universe is tied together, no movement can take place of any particle without it having an effect, however small, on every other particle," our bodies are very small universes and obey the same laws. When one human universe touches another it projects its vibrations just as one planet affects another or one sun another. Unless this fact of living response to life is grasped the chief point of Abrams' system is lost. Many of Abrams' followers are now engaged in trying to devise apparatus to entirely eliminate the human elements. They may contrive to invent some interesting and useful instrument, but they will only be able to observe the electrical effects of life. The phenomena of life itself will be lost. I will now describe my own circuit in detail : The objects aimed at were (1) to preserve Abrams' use of life forces ; (2) his use of figures ; (3) increase of the impulse ; (4) protection from outside forces.

We may roughly regard the circuit as a wireless set if we are not too pedantic about the term "wireless." At any rate to do so will make the description easier for the man in the street, if it offends more scientific minds.

The transmitting station is the patient's body, or the specimen being tested ; the wires to the tuning apparatus can be compared to the aerial ; the valve set is the amplifier, and the subject or human being, whose muscles, when tapped or stroked, interpret the signals given off, may be compared to the loud-speaker or earphones. This analogy must not be carried too far. We are not trying to pick up the B.B.C. but to ascertain, by the measured reflexes of the human abdomen, the balances in the human body or alterations which indicate the kind of disease present.

The circuit which I now use is considerably more elaborate than Abrams' original one. The system is operated inside a cage of perforated zinc, which cage is placed on glass piano supports. The frame is of wood, with zinc mesh screens for walls ; these and the frame are all earthed. I found that this was necessary in order to prevent emanations from persons, drugs, and other objects in the room, from interfering with the tests.

The patient sits in one compartment of the cage ; the operator, his instruments, and the subject, are in another. The patient sits on a plate, connected to the circuit by a wire, and places an electrode, attached by a separate wire, over the part to be tested. The chair on which the patient sits contains no metal, and all metals should be removed from the patient's person before he is tested.

The circuit for detecting emanations from the patient consists of three parts :—

(a) The primary circuit, including the patient, dynamiser

(a box to hold the specimens used in absence of the patient), and certain tuning apparatus ;

(*b*) An amplifier ;

(*c*) The secondary circuit.

The terms "primary" and "secondary circuits" are used for purposes of description, and it is not intended to imply any connection between the two parts of the circuit, such as occurs for instance between the primary and secondary circuits of a transformer.

The patient acting as a transmitting station, his emanations oscillate in the circuit, formed as follows (*see* fig. 1) :—

(*a*) *The Primary Circuit.*—This refers to the circuit connected with the input of oscillations to the amplifier.

I.—A wire passes from the electrode (1), held over the part being tested, to an electrode (2), in the floor of the dynamiser.

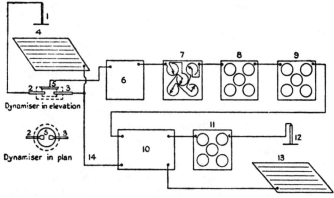

Dynamiser in elevation

Dynamiser in plan

FIG. 1.

A return wire (3), from another electrode in the floor of the dynamiser, goes to the plate (4), on which the patient sits. A return wire from the amplifier (14) is attached to electrode (3), which is attached to the patient's plate. These two electrodes are separated by about an inch. The lid of the dynamiser forms another electrode, which is separated from the electrodes in the floor by about a quarter of an inch.

II.—The wire from the top of the dynamiser (5) passes through the colour box (6). This contains a series of small light bulbs, each covered with a different coloured shade, and each with a separate switch, so that various colours in turn can be flashed on to the wire passing through the box.

III.—The wire from the colour box then passes through three or more dial resistance boxes (7, 8, 9), with studs to give five figure settings in ohms. The first rheostat has straight wires, the second and third non-inductively wound coils.

(b) *The Amplifier* (10 in fig. 1).—The amplifier is a three--stage high-frequency amplifier, designed to amplify very short wave-lengths, i.e. about the order of three to four metres. The circuit is shown in the accompanying fig. 2. Coils, numbered (3) and (4), are single-turn coils, about one inch in diameter, closely coupled together. (10) is an ordinary 100-turn wireless coil, such as may be purchased of any wireless dealer, with a diameter of about two and a half inches ; (11) is a similar coil of 250 turns ; (10) and (11) are vario-coupled, and are usually operated with the plane of the coils inclined at about 30° .

(c) *The Secondary Circuit.*—The output from the amplifier has one leg connected through a measuring rheostat (11, fig. 1)

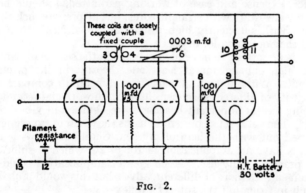

FIG. 2.

to a small metal disc, about the size of a shilling (12), which is supported over the forehead of the subject by an insulating headpiece. The disc is separated from the skin over the frontal sinus by a rubber cup, which causes a gap of about 3 inches between the disc and the skin. The other leg of the output is connected to a plate (13), under the feet of the subject.

NOTES ON THE CIRCUIT.

(1) The gap between the electrodes of the dynamiser causes an amplification of the effect of the oscillation from the patient. The gap on the subject's forehead has the same effect.

Abrams probably discovered this experimentally, but he has not left any record giving reasons for the details of the apparatus which he designed.

Apparatus similar to the dynamiser has been used in work on high-frequency waves.

(2) In ordinary practice it is sufficient to have four colours : red, yellow, green and blue, in the colour box, for testing. In selecting colours for treatment a large number of shades are needed, and these can be thrown on to the circuit by means of coloured screens and a torch.

(3) The rheostats which I use are wound in ohms and accurately graduated. They are wound non-inductively. The first in the series has straight wires. This gives the best reactions on the subject. It goes up to 1111·1 ohms and allows a setting of $\frac{1}{100}$ of an ohm, so that any element can be tuned into on its atomic weight to two decimal places.

The other rheostats in the primary circuit go up to 99,999 ohms, the one in the secondary circuit to 111,111 ohms. If space, expense and ease of working permitted, I should have all my rheostats with straight wires, but at present such rheostats, with sufficiently high resistance, are difficult to make and they occupy a lot of space.

It is important to have high ohmage in the secondary circuit and high ohmage for at least one rheostat in the primary circuit. Without high ohmage it is difficult to compare the intensity of different specimens in research work and secondary tuning has an important bearing on recognition of vibrations.

(4) The valve set at present in use is the result of experiments carried out with the help of my son, Gerald Richards. The valves have an amplification factor of 20, which is sufficient for practical daily use. Much greater amplification could be obtained with more or different valves, but this would probably result in tiring out the subject's reflexes.

(5) The coils have already been described.

(6) Each rheostat should have 5 figures, otherwise it is impossible to distinguish between some substances, for instance indium registers on 88,061 ohms and scrophularia on 88,060. Ten figures might be better; but so far we have not found two substances giving the same highest intensity frequency.

(7) Before I used a valve set I had a crystal set, such as is used in wireless reception, between the subject and the secondary circuit rheostat, to cut him off from the circuit. This is an additional safeguard but is not needed with a valve set.

Screening between the subject and the set is necessary to prevent his emanations from passing through the set.

(8) A male subject is preferable as his muscles are usually better developed. He must be physically fit and a man who will take an intelligent interest in the work. Standing for

some hours a day and having the abdomen stroked would be
very tiring to anyone who did not understand what was going
on, and an intelligent subject can be of the greatest assistance.
Women doctors naturally prefer to work with female subjects.

USES OF RHEOSTATS.

(1) The first rheostat is used for the recognition of substances,
elements by their atomic weights expressed in ohms, micro-
organisms by waves worked out from specimens ; glands,
organisms and structures from specimens. For instance,
liver is tuned into on 99,834 and is measured on the rheostat
in the secondary circuit in order to ascertain whether there
is normal balance, i.e. 37 ohms. Similarly, B. influenzæ
is tuned into on 99,880 and measured to see whether there
is an increase in its specific frequency or not.

This frequency is normally present in the body and, presumably, all other frequencies in the bacillus are present in the
body, but an infection alters the normal balance and so indicates the presence of an organism. This fact can be tested
experimentally by giving someone a culture of B. influenzæ
to hold in the hand or to place against some part of the body
and, on measuring up, it is possible to tell against which part
of the body the culture was placed.

(2) The second rheostat is used for localising the infection.
Suppose a Morgan infection = 74 ohms is found and the liver
is suspected, then 99,834, the local call for liver, is put up on
the second rheostat. If the normal measurement of 37 ohms
is obtained the liver is free, if badly infected an intensity of
74 ohms may be found.

Every part of the body gives a local tuning wave, and these
are gradually being worked out.

(3) The third rheostat gives still finer tuning. Suppose
the heart is affected. The general heart-rate is up on the
second rheostat, on the third rheostat the rates for nerve,
muscle, valve can be put up in turn and the special system
affected thus discovered.

In some kinds of research five and even more rheostats
are needed.

NATURE OF THE REFLEX FELT.

The changes in the abdominal wall of the subject feel
to me like a contraction of the muscular wall. Other
operators, however, describe somewhat different sensations.
Abrams, by using a rabbit's ear, showed that there were

changes in the blood supply. He also showed that in an animal under an anæsthetic changes took place in the wall of the intestine when stimulated through the head, just as the subject is stimulated. Probably all tissues are affected in a certain area.

Whatever changes take place the abdominal wall muscles are involved, as the difference between a good muscular wall and a slack one is marked.

The areas affected vary with different wave-lengths, the shape of the hardened areas vary, sometimes a ridge is formed, sometimes a small lump, like a pea is felt.

Stroking the abdomen is the method which I use for eliciting the reflex ; it is quicker and extraneous noises matter far less than when the percussion method is employed. Moreover, having been a surgeon for a good part of my life, my finger-tips are more sensitive than my ears.

EFFECT OF THE EARTH'S MAGNETIC FIELD.

During the operation the subject must face geographical west. If he turns north or south the reflex disappears. The best position for the subject and the set of instruments is at right-angles to geographical north, not to the magnetic north.

The action of the earth's magnetic field on metals, especially iron, is common knowledge, but its effect on our bodies is not so well known. Since the reflexes we are using are affected by magnets it is not surprising to find that they are affected by the earth's magnetic forces.

Some people can only sleep comfortably while lying north and south. I once had a small patient, aged four, who refused to sleep in any other position.

A. E. Baines, when he was examining a persistently anæmic patient with a galvanometer, found that the steel in her stays had become magnets. The stays were discarded and she recovered without further treatment.

EARTHING.

As I have already said, the protecting cage, the table the set is on, and the screen in the cage are all earthed.

A better reflex is perhaps obtained when operator and subject are also earthed, but this is not essential, and the disadvantages to health of being earthed for hours at a time are considerable.

SCREENING.

One criticism of my method of the circuit remains to be considered. Dr. Boyd lays stress on the necessity for cutting off the operator from the subject by screening except where it is essential that they should touch, i.e. the operator's hands and the subject's abdomen. Boyd meets this by having the operator outside the cage, and makes contact with the subject by putting his arms through woven metal gauze sleeves attached to the cage.

, My answer to this criticism is that we have proved, time after time, that no reaction takes place until a specimen is put in the circuit, except a fraction of an ohm of aluminium which comes from the circuit itself. Further, anything coming from the operator will pass through his fingers to the subject, whether the rest of his body be screened or not.

In my opinion it is far more important to have the operator inside the cage where he and the whole system is guarded from external effects. Boyd secures cover for himself and his instruments by working in a screened room, but so far I have not found this to be necessary.

Boyd's methods are wonderful in their meticulous accuracy and care. My circuit, however, acts in a somewhat different way from the emanometer.

THE USE OF THE OHM IN TUNING.

The emanometer designed by Boyd appeals to the wireless expert more than any variety of Abrams' circuit because tuning is secured by condensers as in a wireless set.

I have adhered to tuning by ohms, because I found that figures had a definite significance. It has been pointed out to me that to tune in ohms is an outrageous proceeding as it is entirely new to wireless methods. However, I am content to follow the founder of the method in his outrageous proceedings, for the practical results so obtained are good.

Abrams was undoubtedly a genius and it is the habit of genius to stumble on methods which, at first sight, appear absurd, but later are found to be the best for the purpose.

Boyd and other users of the emanometer have done a great work ; it is all to the good that different methods should be used. If, however, you forsake the methods of a genius in their essentials you run the risk of losing something important.

By ceasing to use figures workers using the emanometer are apt to lose contact with a world whose forces can be expressed in mathematical formulæ. The use of figures appears to me to be too important to be neglected, and everyday my experiences confirm this opinion.

I shall be very glad of any suggestions which would improve the circuit. For daily use it is sufficient, but for demonstrations, or to replace the subject with some mechanical detector, a further magnification is probably desirable. To increase the amplification a great deal for daily use might tire out the reflexes of the subject, also it might be injurious to health, for the subject is receiving emanations which are the result of disease. When a cancer case is tested the subject's magnetic field should be treated with a magnet or by the operator's hands.

I must add a few remarks on the theory of how the circuit works, for though, from my ignorance of physics, I am a very unfit person to do so, I have experimented and have some evidence to offer. What is the evidence ?

(1) We use for our tuning coils the unit of resistance. Therefore presumably the circuit is working by means of resistance.

(2) It has been found that when coils are used they should be wound non-inductively. If the circuit were worked by inductance surely the coils would be best wound inductively.

(3) A straight wire rheostat gives a cleaner cut reflex than a coil, and the intensity of output, measured in ohms in the secondary circuit, is higher when a straight wire is used than when a coil is used with the same ohmage. A straight-wire rheostat was made by Gambrell Bros., on Colonel Lefroy's suggestion, to test the effect of capacity. An increase of capacity which a coil gives appears to blur the hardness of the reflex.

So far resistance appears to be of the greatest importance, but I will now describe the action of life-forces.

(4) A dead *B. morgan* culture will tune to a figure 97,979. If this be then placed on a second rheostat in series, the reflex cannot be obtained ; the same happens with minerals. If however the *B. morgan* be alive the figure 97,979 can be placed on two rheostats in series, and the reflex obtained is harder than before. At first sight this appears to rule out resistance, for we have apparently increased resistance. I am not sure that it is safe to argue this way in this form of vital physics. What we call " dead matter " acts, more or less in my circuit as we might expect it to do, by ordinary physical laws, but when we come to live matter there is a difference. Matter that is actually living has some quality of activity absent in dead matter.

If you look on the ohm's mass effect as a collection of electrons in movement in a confined space, may not life-force so stimulate the electrons that the impulse is passed on through similar groups of electrons again, until it reaches a live indicator, the muscles of the subject's abdomen ?

I shall, in the chapter on biomorphs, show that live matter radiates other forces than those from protons and electrons. These may act in a manner similar to ionisation.

Abrams thought his circuit was acting by resistance ; perhaps he was right. In any case I must leave the final decision on this point for other and wiser heads than mine. I would only ask those who criticise, or those who work at the circuit, to remember that we are using life-forces when we use a human subject. Results may be different without him. The primary object is not to settle points in physics, but to study the human body and its auric forces, and such others as we may be able to tap. In dealing with a fresh branch of study it is wisest to accumulate evidence and to go slow on explanations.

CHAPTER IV

THE ATOM AND THE OHM

AFTER studying Abrams' work for some time, I was persuaded that he was dealing with important issues, and I had an oscilloclast installed in my house. I treated patients by this means, but soon came to the conclusion that I was working very much in the dark. The results were good, often very good, but I had little idea of what was really happening. This ignorance, when using a new form of treatment became distressing, more distressing than the ignorance which is felt when following a well-beaten track, and here, in this new field, there were but few footmarks to lend assurance. To gain more knowledge seemed an imperative need, for Abrams and his apparatus were already under a withering fire of hostile criticism.

What were these waves which I received on my indicator? What did 55, 50, 42 and so on mean? The body was obviously the most complicated mechanism. Anything might come from it. I must try something simpler; make experiments with less complicated mechanisms. Abrams' facts, so far as they went, were correct. When the patient had cancer, a reaction was recorded on the subject with the rheostat set at 50 ohms resistance in most cases. So were his other statements correct, but what did they mean?

After spending many hours examining various elements I made the astonishing discovery that the atomic numbers of elements corresponded to the figures on my rheostats when I was tuning in on my circuit : that is hydrogen, the first element, caused a reflex on 1 ohm, oxygen on 8 ohms, sodium on 11, sulphur on 16, and so on.

Before describing my experiences which led up to this discovery, it seems desirable to say a few words about the atomic number and the ohm.

Long before modern research on the atom had shown that hydrogen had one electron, helium two, lithium three, beryllium four, barium five and so on, the elements which had been discovered had been placed in their present position in the atomic table on chemical grounds. The atomic number therefore indicates the place of the element in the table ; it also gives the number of electrons possessed by the element.

The view that the atomic numbers are merely relative I do not need to discuss ; it appears to have been dropped, and does not concern me. I can tune in my apparatus to hydrogen on 1 ohm, 100 ohms, and any multiple in hundreds, up to 100,000,000 ohms : all give an equal intensity on the secondary circuit rheostat, but the reflex is harder with 100,000,000 ohms than with lesser figures.

We all know that the ohm is the unit of resistance. It is a resistance that will produce one ampere of current, when one volt is passed through it. It is actually represented by a column of mercury 106·3 centimetres long, 14·4521 grammes in mass at 0° C. Obviously one would say a convention, not on actuality like the atomic number. The ohm has been evaluated at a number of international conferences, and numbers of experiments made to secure a satisfactory measure.

When I read a description of some of the work done I felt that some of the workers had made an attempt to reach something which had a relationship to the natural forces of the earth. However that may be, when a physicist says that the chances are very considerably against the atomic number and the ohm corresponding I agree. But however unlikely the correspondence may be, it is the duty of a research worker to record his results quite regardless of anyone else accepting them, or explaining them by theories with which he may not agree.

The discovery, whatever the explanation, has proved of the greatest value to my work. Before discussing possible explanations I will describe how I came to make the discovery, and its practical results in treatment.

I started a long series of experiments with elements. I collected a number, finally 42. My method was to put the element in the dynamiser and turn my rheostat stud from 1 onwards, noting at which numbers I obtained a reflex on my subject's muscles. I found that different numbers caused reflexes of varied intensity. This was a long and laborious business. The elements with the larger nuclei gave a large number of reflexes.

The relationship between the atomic number and the ohm in tuning did not show up at once. It was not till I had studied my charts of atomic action that I discovered that all the elements tested gave a reaction on the atomic number, and that when this figure was used the secondary tuning was higher than with other figures I had obtained. With sulphur, for instance, I got a reflex on 10, 16, 20, 30, 32, 50, 60 and so on. I will deal with the significance of the 10, 20 series later on. Later I found that I got a somewhat harder reflex when I tuned with 32·06, the average atomic weight, than with 32. It took me some time to find out that this correlation was a universal rule.

I then started to examine the polarity of the reactions caused by elements when tuned to the different numbers. I found that all elements caused a negative reaction when their atomic number was on the rheostat, on the right-hand side of the abdomen, and a positive reaction on the left, when the atomic weight figures were hoisted. A negative reaction is one which is repelled by the negative, or south-seeking pole of the magnet, and attracted by the north-seeking pole. A positive reaction is repelled by the north-seeking pole and attracted by the south-seeking pole.

This discovery only came after prolonged search, as at first I did not appreciate the importance of intensity, i.e. the relative strength of reactions. I had to become familiar with the apparatus I was using. The discovery was the result of my desire to find out what Abrams' figures meant.

Having discovered that the elements could be recognised in this way, the next point was to see if Abrams' figures, by which he recognised different diseases, could be affected by the elements which they apparently represented. He recognised acquired syphilis by the figure 55 ; I found that this was affected by introducing cæsium. Then 50 was the figure by which he recognised cancer, and I found this was affected by tin, the fiftieth element.

In one cancer case I obtained an important reaction on 29. I had no copper available except a copper electrode, and this only annulled the reaction when held about four feet over the circuit. This led to the discovery of the importance of dilutions and their activity, as I rightly guessed that such action at a distance corresponded to dilution.

Abrams recognised asthma on 29. I found that this reaction was most active on the liver, and was affected by copper dilutions. Later, after studying homœopathic writings, I found that copper had relieved some cases of asthma, and was recognised as an antispasmodic. In some asthma cases the urine produces a deposit when boiled with Fehling's solution, but the deposit is unlike that of diabetic urine.

Koch, in U.S.A., found that guanidin plays an important part in cancer, and all cancer cases give an increased reaction for guanidin, on 59·06, its molecular weight. Urea is correspondingly decreased, judged by the reactions found on 60·05 ohms, the molecular weight of urea. In gout, and cases in which one would expect an increase of uric acid, I find an increased reaction for 168·07, the molecular weight of uric acid. This discovery of reactions on molecular weights led me to study the intestinal flora by this means. In the chapter on inflammatory disease I give a table showing the sugar reactions for various organisms, worked out on these molecular weights. This was my earliest method of separating out the infections, working on the lines of a chemical table. I found that if an organism did not give a lactose reaction 360·19 it would not ferment lactose.

' This method was most fruitful clinically, and also explained what Abrams' numbers meant. What he had picked up happened to be an atomic number ; had he gone further he would have got all sorts of numbers : at that stage he might have become confused. It is however quite clear that a serious disease, like syphilis or cancer, could not affect merely one atom or one compound ; indeed they affect nearly every element in the body in varying degrees.

In my early years of work I spent much time analysing blood or specimens of various diseases, on atomic numbers or atomic weights. One table is given under cancer.

With minerals in the testing circuit the energy from the negative reaction or the lump on the abdomen caused by hoisting the atomic number, equals the energy caused by the positive reaction of the atomic weight number, i.e.

> 16, −, = 32·06, +, when sulphur is examined ;
> 50, −, = 118·7, + for tin ;
> 8, −, = 16, +, for oxygen ;
> 11, −, = 23, +, for sodium ;
> 55, -, = 132·81, +, for cæsium.

All elements tested acted in the same way.

I deducted from this that the positive reactions represented the nuclear energy, and the negative reactions, on the atomic number, equalled the total electronic energy on the negative side of the atom. I shall go into greater detail later on, with regard to the nature of the atom as examined by my circuit.

Having obtained a proof of the general soundness of my discovery I was able to go ahead with greater confidence.

Instead of having a set of numbers which might mean anything, I had a key to Abrams' discoveries and a sound and understandable method for the examination of the human body.

I have used this method now for so many years and with such excellent results that I have in the meantime lost sight of the fact that the correspondence of the ohm and atomic number, atomic weight, etc., must sound strange to others who have always regarded the ohm as a purely arbitrary measure.

Mr. Dudley Wright, F.R.C.S., when working with me, picked out elements correctly by this method, when neither he nor the subject knew what was present. I have done the same myself, but not always correctly, for mind comes in and upsets results, and there are certain technical pitfalls.

It has been suggested to me that this discovery of the atom and ohm correspondence, and in fact all my reactions are purely mental reactions ; that they exist on another plane to protons and electrons of the physical world. To this I reply :—

(1) That I can work out a case by employing actual substances in place of numbers ;

(2) That I have found myself able to distinguish between mental action and physical action, when looking out for it (*see* chapter on the action of the mind) ;

(3) That I have clinical and laboratory support for the results ;

(4) That, though I am ready to realise the important action of subconscious control, results in research do not come to me till I have put in many hours of conscious research ;

(5) That in my research I did not reach any conclusion till after many months of laborious experiment, using apparently, physical means ;

(6) That even if there were subconscious guidance this does not invalidate the results. Most research students will agree that their most serviceable results come when they have put aside a problem for a time, and then one fine morning find it solved for them.

I quite agree that the use of a human subject and a human being's hands bring in elements outside ordinary physics, but at the same time the human frame is partly earthly and subject to the laws of Nature, commonly known as physics, even though it transcends them in some ways. Also if there be counterparts to human physics on another plane, this is no reason for denying the presence of the physical plane in my experiments.

It is always safest in experiments to seek the easiest explanation first, and in dealing with any kind of phenomena I prefer not to exclude the physical before I accept more occult explanations.

It is easier to believe that I obtained actual physical results in my research and do so daily than to believe that I was guided simply by some form of clairvoyance and am so guided in obtaining clinical results. There are some of my esteemed colleagues, a large group in America, who hold to the super-physical theory. I disagree with them. I do not deny that they, or any kind of healer, may have special powers—any of us may be helped in our work—but I think that such a claim has grave dangers. Let us try to explain phenomena by physical means first. The almost uncanny rightness of some physicians for selecting the right remedy may be allied to clairvoyance, but it does not come to them without years of study and observation. Any discovery I have made has only been after months of laborious work. If one attributes phenomena to special personal powers one limits the field of usefulness of a discovery. The correspondence of the ohm and the atomic number has been useful to many others in their work.

CHAPTER V

THE HUMAN ATOMIC TABLE

BEFORE getting to what are perhaps the more interesting parts of my research I must relate work done on the atomic table. This work was undertaken as far as I can remember for two reasons, to elucidate work being done in America and because I felt on studying Bohr's table as given in Professor Andrade's " Structure of the Atom," that this table was incomplete and that man's structure might reveal evidence of yet more complicated atoms.

As my readers may have forgotten some of the chemistry they learnt at school I give the atomic table as given in chemistry textbooks. In fig. 3 elements which closely resemble each other in their chemical action are placed under one another; others with less resemblance are placed to right or left. Thus the alkaline metals, lithium, sodium, potassium, rubidium and cæsium, come under one another. Copper, silver and gold are to one side. There are seven periods, placed vertically and extending horizontally. The first element in each group is an alkali and the last an inert gas.

In fig. 4 these seven periods are shown in a different arrangement. Bohr, who was the author of this table, was regarding the relationship of the elements not as a chemist but as a physicist. The dark figures are those given by Bohr, the fainter figures are mine, but Bohr did state that if ever the seventh period was completed it would end with 118.

The faint lines show connections as worked out by reflexes.

If you study Bohr's table it will strike you at once that it appears incomplete ; in six periods the first element is an alkali and the last an inert gas which will combine with no other element. Where is the seventh gas to complete the period ? Obviously the six known elements in the seventh period form only a portion, 92 uranium is the last known element.

When I had studied various books on the subject I started to try and work out the problem on abdominal reflexes.

Hardin, Hayward and Du Plessis in U.S.A. had published a number of new recognition numbers for organs and glands. Thyroid has been recognised by Abrams on 6 ohms, later 166 was given as the recognition number, 144 was given for

	I.	II.	III.	IV.	V.	VI.	VII.	VIII. (a)	VIII. (b)	VIII. (c)	O.
1	1 H. 1.008										2 He. 4.00
2	3 Li. 6.94	4 Be. 9.02	5 B. 10.82	6 C. 12.00	7 N. 14.01	8 O. 16.00	9 F. 19.0				10 Ne. 20.2
3	11 Na. 22.997	12 Mg. 24.32	13 Al 26.97	14 Si. 28.06	15 P. 31.02	16 S. 32.06	17 Cl. 35.46				18 A. 39.91
4	19 K. 39.096	20 Ca. 40.07	21 Sc. 45.1	22 Ti. 48.1	23 V 50.96	24 Cr 52.01	25 Mn. 54.93	26 Fe. 55.84	27 Co. 58.94	28 Ni. 58.69	
	29 Cu. 63.57	30 Zn. 65.38	31 Ga. 69.72	32 Ge. 72.6	33 As. 74.96	34 Se. 79.2	35 Br. 79.92				36 Kr. 82.92
5	37 Rb. 85.44	38 Sr. 87.63	39 Y. 88.9	40 Zr. 91.00	41 Nb. 93.1	42 Mo. 96.0	43 Ma.	44 Ru. 101.7	45 Rh. 102.9	46 Pd. 106.7	
	47 Ag. 107.88	48 Cd. 112.41	49 In. 114.8	50 Sn. 118.7	51 Sb. 121.77	52 Te. 127.5	53 I. 126.932				54 Xe. 130.2
6	55 Cs. 132.81	56 Ba. 137.37	Rare Earths.	72 Hf. 180.80	73 Ta. 181.5	74 W. 184.0	75 Re. (187.3)	76 Os. 190.9	77 Ir. 193.1	78 Pt. 195.2	
	79 Au. 197.2	80 Hg. 200.6	81 Tl. 204.39	82 Pb. 207.20	83 Bi. 209.00	84 Po (210.0)	85— 216.20				86 Rn. (222.0)
7	87— (223.04)	88 Ra. 226.0	89 Ac. (226)	90 Th. 232.15	91 Pa. (230)	92 U. 238.17					
RARE EARTHS.	57 La. 139.0	58 Ce. 140.25	59 Pr. 140.9	60 Nd. 144.27	61 Il. (148.20)	62 Sm. 150.4	63 Eu. 152.0	64 Gd. 157.3			
	65 Tb. 159.2	66 Dy. 162.5	67 Ho. 163.5	68 Er. 167.7	69 Tm. 169.4	70 Yb. 173.5	71 Lu. 175.0				

Fig 3.—The Atomic Table.

parathyroid and so on.   I suspected that these figures might be due to atoms.   I found that 6 and 166 varied in intensity in an exactly similar way, if 6 was up so was 166, and to the same degree.

It would be tedious if I described all my experiments, but I studied the known elements and found that the elements which were periodic caused reflexes on one area.   For instance the halogens all reacted on one area, the sulphur, selenium tellurium group on another.   There were other correspondences which I need not describe here, but it was a matter of gradually carrying these across the border into the unknown territory.

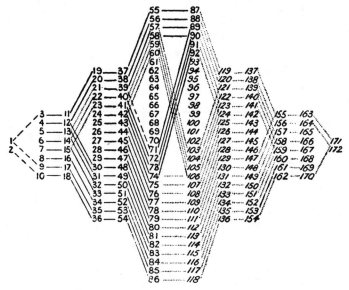

FIG. 4.—The Human Atomic Table.

When I started my investigation I put aside all I had read and forgot about Bohr's 118 ; if I had remembered it I should have been saved much labour.   I felt sure that after a bit I should get a balanced table, but what point was the centre and where the table would end were the questions I asked myself.   Only when I had obtained the outline of my scheme did I again look at Bohr's table.

On theory alone the sixth period might form a centre group with five periods on each side.

I drew up such a table, but it would not work on the rules I formed for myself. Remember I had cut myself adrift from all books and was deliberately forgetting anything I might have learnt from them.

It may be suggested that the subconscious knowledge was there and in time it worked, the way it worked is rather interesting.

When I had collected a great deal of data, and had worked out many series of elements with regard to the reflexes obtained from them, I was forced to put aside my research for professional work for some time. After a hard morning's work I tried to switch off from everything connected with wireless reactions, and to rest my mind read an article on " Gothic Architecture " by Sydney Klein. The writer describes how architects worked on masonic symbolism and how certain cathedrals were built on the plan of the two triangles placed base to base. The two triangles together represented a fish, $\iota\chi\theta\upsilon\varsigma$, symbol of the soul, and later of Jesus Christ, the Son of God. The chapter ended by saying that God is the Great Geometrist. With this thought in my mind I fell asleep, and on waking, whilst I was still but half awake, I saw my table of the two triangles, base to base, with the elements arranged within it. I was still, for a time, immersed in professional work, but about a week later, again in a semi-waking state, I saw my triangles, base to base, containing all the elements, known and unknown, in their twelve periods. I then returned to my research and found that my collected data indicated the presence of 172 elements in the human body. This was in accordance with my table, complete and symmetrical. The question at once presents itself : Do the atoms with heavy nuclei exist in the earth ? They must have done so once, or they would not exist in us. Perhaps they have broken down, as radium is now breaking down. This is however uncertain, for Dr. Petrie gives a 172 reaction for hydrogen, 171 for helium, 170 for lithium, 169 for beryllium, 168 for boron, and so on, and I have confirmed this on a number of elements. I think it is unlikely that hydrogen gas is combined with 172 in nature and I regard this as a peculiarity of the human reflexes. I think it is most likely that these two elements are tied closely together in the human body and that when the reflex on 1 ohm is excited by hydrogen this gas also stimulates the 172 mechanism. Similarly, lithium is tied to 170. This is a question which may be settled in the future, but at any rate in man these frequencies have a very close connection.

This connection runs through the entire table in disease ; if 1 is out of balance so is 172 ; if 86 is increased so is 87 ; if 86 is diminished so is 87.

When examining the atomic numbers in the sheep's brain I found the following elements absent : the 49th, 81st, 113th and 131st. In the table 49 corresponds to 113 and 81 to 131.

In some vegetables 38 and 56 were absent, so were 88 and 120. Gaps appear to be always symmetrical. Corresponding numbers on both sides of the table are always absent. Unless I had worked out this atomic table I could not have understood the symmetrical arrangement of the human body.

Nor could I have understood what certain figures meant that were being quoted as being indicative of certain substances. This is of practical importance.

Now we come to another phenomenon which shows how closely the two sides of the table are tied together in the human body.

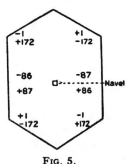

Fig. 5.

If you find the area for hydrogen on 1 ohm on the left side of the abdomen and then put 172 on the tuning rheostat you will get a reflex on this area, but while the reflex with one up causes a negative reaction that with 172 causes a positive reaction. If we examine the corresponding area on the right of the abdomen we find there we get a positive reaction with 1 ohm and a negative reaction with 172. This occurs right through the table from 1 to 172.

The reactions on the abdomen seem at first very complicated, and I have found that for practical purposes it is best to work almost entirely above the navel. Polarities are opposite on the two sides of the abdomen, both above and below the navel. The following summary of the elements and their reflexes on the abdomen should be of use to workers who are following this line of research :—

1 to 86 negative above the navel on right side.
87 to 172 negative above the navel on the left side.
87 to 172 negative below the navel on the right side.
1 to 86 negative below the navel on the left side.

It must also be remembered that every element is duplicated by its opposite polarity double, and this is rather confusing.

We have then in man two sets of elements ; one set gives negative reactions on atomic numbers and the other set positive. One set balances the other.

In addition to the tie between 1 and 172, 2 and 171, and so on, there is a tie between elements situated in similar position on either side of the table ; 6 is tied to 166, 3 to 163, 11 to 155, 19 to 137, 37 to 119, and so on. These vary together in disease and are affected by the introduction into the circuit of their corresponding number.

The numbers 13 to 17 on the oscilloclast, Abrams' vibratory apparatus, if correctly tuned to the elements, have the same effect on other elements as the numbers 157 to 161. This is no accident. (*See* chapters on inflammatory conditions and cancer on action of dispersors).

This phenomenon of a flash from the unconscious mind, supra-conscious we should call it, is not at all uncommon. Most people who have done research work or who have continually worked at any problem will recognise that if one has worked at a problem and then gives it a rest it very often solves itself while you are asleep.

The supra-conscious mind does not sleep. As I shall show later, some portion of the personality leaves us during sleep. It returns as we wake, and in the half-awake condition we retain some memory of what we call dreams. Often a muddled memory. In my case I got a picture because a picture of the table was what I had been seeking.

I will now deal with some further details of the atom as examined by this method.

CHAPTER VI

MORE ABOUT THE ATOM

A S I described in the last chapter I discovered the correspondence between the ohm tuning and the atomic
number after a series of tests on a number of
elements.

I will give the results of a few of these series for two reasons :
firstly that the figures may possibly be of some interest to
those who follow me along some line which I cannot foresee
at present, and secondly because I want to deal with a statement made by chemists in regard to dilutions.

In a paper in the *Homœopathic Journal* of April, 1925,
Dr. Sabbatini is quoted as having traced chemical evidence
of matter up to the 13th centesimal and Dr. Wéjust up to the
24th. Both agree that higher dilutions contain electrons,
but in their opinion electrons in all higher dilutions are all
of the same character.

If all high dilutions merely contained electrons of the
same character, the clinical results of taking an M.M. dilution
of sulphur or silica would be the same, whereas every homœopathic physician knows they are not.

Moreover, anyone who has been given high potencies
knows how rapid their effects are and how severe the reactions
after them may be. I can also show mathematical proof
that high potencies of different substances give an entirely
different set of vibratory waves.

The group oxygen, sulphur, selenium and tellurium are
periodic and give off a similar series of frequencies, as shown
below, on ohms tuning :—

      Oxygen : 10, 20, 30, 50, 60, 70, 91, 51.

      Sulphur : 10, 20, 30, 50, 60, 70, 90, 100, 110, 130,
140, 150, 170, 181, 192, 186.

      Selenium, the same series as far as 170, then : 180,
190, 210, 220, 230, 250, 260, 270, 290, 300, 310, 331, 343,
378, 393, 424, 442, 466, 497, 541.

      Tellurium gives the same series as the others as
regards what I believe to be tuning for the inner electrons.

There are three things to note in these figures :—

(1) They are the same up to a certain point for all the
elements of this group.

(2) When we arrive at a certain point in each group we do not get a serial figure but one slightly higher up ; as we reach the elements with a larger number of electrons the numbers get more spread out, i.e. the satellite is not quite in the position one would expect to find it.   There is a kind of astronomical effect.

(3) Multiples of 40 never occur. This is probably due to the nucleus being grouped in fours making such a position impossible for any electron in this group.

These figures are the same whether solid elements are examined or dilutions as high as an M.M., that is, a thousand thousand dilutions to the power of 100, an almost inconceivable figure to the non-mathematical mind.   Such dilutions are made by machinery.

Even in this extreme attenuation the same frequencies are found as with the solid.   Has the atom been broken up ? All my evidence would suggest that it has not, but I have not the knowledge to really discuss this point ; the atom may have changed its condition, it may be in such a state of increased activity that it has reached a different plane of matter. It may be in a similar state to the frequencies in our aura, retaining at the same time the relative positions of its electrons. This would explain the great clinical effect of high potencies and at the same time explain how they retain specific effects as we know they do in practice. The halogens fluorine, chlorine, bromine and iodine, were also examined.   They show the same features as below :—

9th element fluorine : 23, 30, 37, 44, 51, 58, 65, 73, 82.

17th element chlorine : the same figures up to 65, then 72, 81, 88, 95, 192, 110, 121, 133, 145, 157.

Iodine and bromine begin in the same with a 7 interval and spread out just like the higher elements in the sulphur series.

With sodium and potassium I got a double set of frequencies as if each electron caused a double set of frequencies of varying intensity.

I did hours and weeks of work, not now worth recording ; each group had its own special interval—mercury and zinc have a 5-interval.

Free electrons may all have the same character, but an electron, so long as it is part of an element, has a special character ; this special character is transmitted to dilutions up to an M.M. in all the dilutions I have tested.

If a chemist says there is nothing specific present in an

M.M. dilution, I say there is nothing you can detect by "chemical means." That is a different matter. Clinical experience and the human reflexes show there is something present and that something is extremely active. There is one effect which I must mention—the lighthouse, or day and night effect. Elements, when examined in the circuit, are found to cause a reflex for a few seconds and then there is a rest period. I have some evidence that elements which are periodic have the same day and night periods, for·instance sulphur, selenium and tellurium have 4 seconds on and 3 off. It appears that the atoms have a day and night, though a short one.

CHAPTER VII

POLARITY

I.

THERE are two great forces in the universe, viz. movement towards a centre and movement towards the periphery, the balance between them we know as positive and negative polarity. The outward current from an electrical generator is positive ; the homeward current is negative ; both are necessary to complete the circuit. The principle of polarity runs throughout Nature. The positive force is stimulating, the negative creative and complementary. In our solar system the sun is positive and the planets negative. In mineral atoms the nuclei that correspond to the sun are positive ; the electrons which correspond to the planets are negative. There is polarity in the solar spectrum, the red, orange and yellow rays are positive and the green, blue and violet negative. In the human body the positive side of the elements are diminished in intensity when in contact with red, orange and yellow rays and are increased when in contact with green, blue and violet rays. These colours have the opposite effect on the negative side of the elements (this is of great importance in treatment, especially in cancer). The positive end of the spectrum increases the action of the male gland, while the blue and violet end increases the corresponding female gland. The best colour film for stimulating the testis is an orange flame colour, wratten red 29. The best film I possess for stimulating the ovary is a deep blue, which has a corresponding position in the spectrum to wratten red 29. Spermatozoa are positive, whereas ova are negative. Pollen grains are almost wholly positive, and the ova of plants are similarly negative. Across space the right hand of man acts as the positive pole of a magnet, his left acts like the south pole ; this is reversed in women. This can be proved and tested on the reflexes of the human body or a suspended magnet. If a hand-to-hand test be made with a galvanometer results are less constant, but other factors come in here. A. E. Baines, who examined a large number of people during many years' work with the galvanometer, said that about

75 per cent. of men were positive in the right hand, and 25 per cent. of women. He maintained that there was a close connection between a man being negative in the right hand and a negative mental attitude. From my own experience I should say that pioneers are always of the right-handed positive group and that negative right-handers are best developed on the critical side. Certainly I have seen sparks fly at first contact between these two types of men. Opposites are supposed to attract each other, but this does not appear to be the case between two extreme types at first sight. Polarity exists on other planes than the physical. Consider the emotional side of sex on its lower plane : it is women who have the positive attractive stimulative force. The pretty girl attracts the attention of all susceptible male eyes. When it is a serious business on the higher emotional plane, however, it is the man who is positive and the lady receptive. On the higher mental plane it is the men who do the abstract thinking and stimulate others with new ideas. Women generally excel in executive mental work and fit in well as secretaries or assistants. It will be noted that most doctors are male and most nurses female. But it is not necessary that administrator and executive should be of two different sexes ; many men will best fit into the executive function and carry out the creation of works stimulated by a mind which is positive on the higher plane. Interchanges of polarity may take place during the twenty-four hours. We should function either way at will. Many men who are dominant in their own proper work outside their homes are lamblike at home. Relaxation is pleasant and good, and it secures balance and a fresh supply of positive mental energy for the next day. Day is positive and night negative ; even the atoms have a rest period, as I have described in the last chapter. The universe must have its days and nights entropy is obviously a negative phase. In collective human history we see the forces of contraction and expansion. The gathering of families into clans and tribes, the formation of nations, the exodus of groups to form colonies and fresh nations are all instances of polarity. If the expansive force persists we should have chaos in our affairs. If the cohesive force persisted we should have a clogged mass at the centre. Through every manifestation of matter and consciousness which is within our power of perception we can see the workings of polarity. It's true " 'Tis love that makes the world go round," but what a cloyed mass we should have without a modicum of healthy repulsion.

II

I deal with the effects of polarity and movements of concentration and expansion in the chapters on diseases of the physical body. On the mental side three examples of abnormal action occur to me, and we may term them polarisation. Firstly, the individuals who cannot express themselves ; usually they suffer from some inferiority complex and their vocal movement may be restricted. Secondly, those who are self-concentrated ; often they suffer from self-pity, the worst medical sin. Thirdly, those who suffer from a repressed complex in the mind ; movement has been closed and when pressure rises the force of the suppressed ideas escapes with violence and breaks bounds. In all cases drainage or a safety-valve is needed and a setting-free of the force with direction along healthy channels. In the first place contacts must be made by practice. In the second case by useful work creating an outside mental interest, and in all cases by psychological treatment. Drugs will also assist in most of the cases, for in my experience there is always some physical correspondence to mental action.

III

We must now descend from illustration of the general principle to chemical details.

Let us now consider the polarity of compounds. Certain bodies, when viewed through the polariscope, are optically active, that is, they turn light either to the right or the left ; those which turn light to the right are called dextrorotary, those which turn it to the left are called lævorotary. Substances which do neither are optically non-active. Neutral substances are so, either because they are composed of equal parts of dextro and lævo compounds, or because they are neutral on account of internal compensation, i.e. their molecules are so arranged that one-half of the molecules balance the others.

A convenient set of compounds for the student to study are the tartaric acids, for they have already been studied by chemists and by the great Pasteur in 1860, and we know what we are dealing with. Tartaric acid is known to the chemist in three forms. Its molecular weight is $168·06$.

The arrows indicate the direction in which the molecules are supposed to rotate (*see* page 628, " Mellor's Inorganic Chemistry " for further details).

When using the human abdominal reflexes as an indicator

for studying chemistry I have found that if the abdomen be divided by two lines drawn through the navel at right angles, positive reactions are obtained in the left upper quadrant (LA in diagram of abdomen) and in the right lower quadrant (RB). Negative reactions are obtained in the right upper quadrant (RA) and left lower quadrant (LB). Neutral reactions are obtained along the median line of the abdomen (RNP). There are two kinds of neutral reactions, one set on RN (ribs to navel), which are connected with lævorotary human compounds and another set which give reactions on NP (navel to pubes) which are connected with dextro compounds. In disease when lævo compounds are increased at

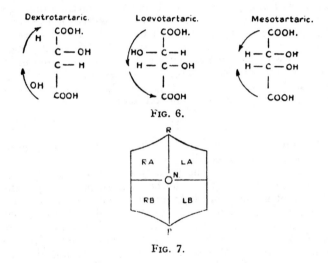

Fig. 6.

Fig. 7.

the expense of dextro, the neutral compounds measured on RN are also increased and those on NP decreased. Polarity may be regarded as movement; if flow of current is interfered with there is trouble.

If examination is made of these tartaric acids on our circuit with 168·06 ohms their molecular weight, on the rheostat :—

Dextrotartaric causes a reflex on LA.RB and NP.

Lævotartaric causes a reflex on RA.LB and RN.

Mesotartaric causes a reflex on NP only.

Mesotartaric is therefore a neutral form allied to dextrotartaric. If racemic acid is examined on 168·06 ohms, reflexes on all four areas are recorded, and on RN and NP, for it contains both dextro- and lævo-tartaric acids in equal quantities. Our reflexes show that the neutral body which tunes in on NP is allied to the lævo body.

The picture formulæ given for these acids in Perkin and Kippins' " Organic Chemistry," p. 274, shows the following, which is accepted by chemists for dextro-, lævo-, and meso-tartaric acid (b). We have to add another picture for meso-tartaric (a). This is present in the human body.

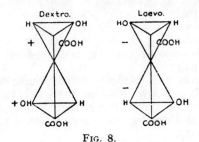

FIG. 8.

If we examine mesotartaric acid further on 84·03 ohms we get reflexes on RA and La which are of equal intensity, showing that its two halves balance.

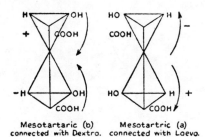

Mesotartaric (b)   Mesotartric (a)
connected with Dextro. connected with Loevo.

FIG. 9.

The first thing to grasp is that lævotartaric is the looking-glass image of dextro, and neutral tartaric (a) of neutral tartaric (b). Although chemistry books maintain that only one form of mesotartaric acid can exist this is not so. Two forms exist in the body.

Racemic acid gives us reflexes for positive, negative and two neutral forms.

More detailed examination of lævotartaric acids will show that the carbon at the centre of the molecule is negative, and that the OH radicles which are negative in dextro- are positive in lævotartaric.

When we place racemic acid in the circuit we get 168·06 reactions equal to each other, on each side of the abdomen.

Now, when we find from our studies of chemical compounds outside the body, that we have looking-glass compounds equal and opposite in every kind of polarity, is it surprising that we find the same thing in the body ? And, further, that there is a universal rule " for every positive there is a negative," " male and female created He them." Where a male body differs from a female body there is always a counterpart in the female of the opposite polarity, and together they make a symmetrical pair.

I will discuss this in detail when dealing with internal secretions. If it is now firmly understood that all frequencies in the human body are positive or negative and that there can be two neutral waves, we are ready to discuss balance within the human body.

CHAPTER VIII

BALANCE

IT is a common saying that a healthy person must be balanced in body and mind. A healthy body is literally balanced chemically.

Working on the centre just above the eyes, which Abrams called the S.V. area, all substances balance at 37 ohms + and −.

The figures below show the reactions for sulphur on the abdomen when measured just above the navel :—

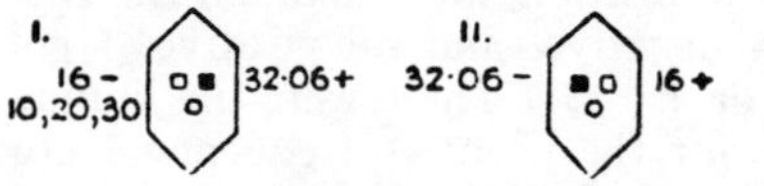

Fig. 10.

from human and animal tissues.

In addition we get the electronic series 10, 20, 30 negative on the left and positive on the right.

This is the case with all elements.

Man possesses elements which have positive nuclei and negative electrons such as we find in metals out of the body and also elements with negative nuclei and positive electrons.

That is we have in us ordinary sulphur, sodium and silica and reversed polarity sulphur, sodium and silica.

Every compound we possess is balanced positively and negatively. In plants, as is known to chemists, dextro or lævo alkaloids exist in a state of unbalance, one or the other may be in excess, hence the clinical effect of certain drugs.

The idea of elements with reversed polarity is really no more strange than compounds with reversed polarity. Science has hitherto studied the elements outside the body and has only dealt with elements with a positive nuclei ; there is, however, no doubt about the body balances.

Before discussing further the question of balances, I must state my belief that the body consists of a number of substances with different balance points. These may be called different colloidal conditions. I discovered a number of these when I was searching for biomorphs. Abrams found that he obtained three different sets of reactions when he placed the receiving electrode on the subject :—

(1) On the forehead above the nose.

(2) At a point at the top of the forehead where the hair generally begins.

(3) On the top of the head where the parietal bone joins the frontal (the place where you find an open spot between the bones in a baby's head).

I found that all these gave different balance points in a healthy person.

(1) Balanced at 37 ohms positively and negatively.

(2) Balanced at 50 ohms positively and negatively.

(3) Balanced at 40 ohms positively and negatively.

On examining patients with some disease I found that in each case there was a constant figure always double the balance point, beyond which reactions were never recorded. If I got an indication for cinnamon on the 37 area which measured 74 negative, and nil positive, I got 100 on No. 2 area and 80 on No. 3. These were the limits. If I obtained lower figures for the negative frequency I always got figures which together made 74, 100 and 80 when added together. If cinnamon was 60 negative, it was 14 positive on the 37 area and so on. Further search revealed eleven areas on the head and eleven areas on the spine which gave eleven different balances. There may be more, but these are enough for the present. Here is the table with the areas and balance points marked.

CENTRES FOR RECEPTION OF FREQUENCIES.

Position		Normal frequency in ohms	Limit of displacement
Mid line head	On spine		
1. Frontal sinus	7th cervical	37	74
2. Mid forehead	2nd dorsal	10	20
3. Just above 2	3rd dorsal	7	14
4. Where hair begins	5th dorsal	50	100
5. Where parietal bone joins frontal, i.e. anterior fontanelle	1st lumbar	40	80
6. Halfway between 5 and 7	Last lumbar	98	196
7. Junction of parietal and occipital bones	2nd lumbar	30	60
8. Occipital protuberance	8th dorsal	74	148
9. Lower edge of 8	7th dorsal	60	120
10. Halfway between 9 and 11	Mid-point sacrum	25	50
11. Base of skull where it joins neck	5th sacral	47	94

What do these various balances mean ? They correspond, I believe, with different kinds of dilution. Of course a great deal of work would have to be done to prove this, and I have only been able to judge by effects and measurements on patients. What I judge by this is that colloidal preparations will correct the lower balances, whereas it takes higher dilutions to correct the higher when the loss of balance in them is considerable. Sometimes all those examined are out of balance, and sometimes I have found that I have corrected the lower balances and not the higher, which require more potent stimulation. It has been noticed clinically, by others as well as myself, that a patient sometimes requires a drug to be given in three or four different states before he is cured. This, I think, points to the necessity for correcting a number of different states in some patients.

This does not exhaust the different colloids in the body ; there may be others that vary in health and disease. I am not going to search for them at present. I have enough for practical purposes and sufficient to show the marvellous variety of states in our human cosmos.

There is a certain colloidal condition, as we will call it, which balances at 60 ohms on secondary tuning positively and negatively which does not vary in disease. This is measured on an area above the subject's ears, the motor area of the brain. I have evidence that this condition continues throughout life. The frequencies obtained on this region on the subject are distinctive of the individual, they are different on the two sides of the subject's head, and they give a clue to the kind of trouble he or she is likely to have. Properly these frequencies should be considered as " birthmarks " ; in the testing cage I refer to them as " *Dhobi marks* " because they do not change *in the wash.* Hereditary connections between parents and children can be traced. Anacardium is a drug which is very useful in treating myself, and two of my sons have the anacardium frequency as a birthmark. Conversely one sometimes finds that a parent's birthmark frequency will indicate a very useful drug for a child. In a patient with syphilis I found frequencies corresponding with salvarsan on one side and fluoric acid on the other. In a patient whose career in the past certainly showed lack of grit and fighting qualities I found a silica frequency. Birthmark frequencies if given as remedies always do some good, but naturally they do not cover the whole ground. In the case of the salvarsan patient I think the birthmark indicated that he was a ready subject for syphilis, and if he acquired it he would have a lot of trouble from it.

How one frequency can be stable in one colloid condition

and out of balance in another is quite beyond me; I only know that the measurements are as I state.

Colour frequencies I have dealt with fully in the chapter on Colour. They appear to balance in the same way as other frequencies, i.e. positively and negatively.

This certainly occurs clinically and in the next chapter, on Secondary Tuning, I describe how this can be recognised.

Alterations in balance when slight = 74 when added together, i.e. if thyroid be slightly subnormal the positive reaction = 35 and negative 39.

When there is a considerable degree of hyperthyroidism I find 74 + reaction on both sides of the abdomen.

If an organ such as the uterus measures 74 + on both sides of the abdomen we should expect the presence of the cancer virus.

If it measures 74 neutral I should expect to find cancer toxins.

The frequency 97979 = 74 + +, i.e. double positive indicates the presence of a live Morgan bacillus.

Ovarian 2 + 2 + indicates a very much reduced ovarian secretion.

In cancer when guanidin 59·06 measures 74 + + urea 60·05 = 74 − − this appears to indicate the absence of positive urea and an excess of the negative or reverse polarity compound.

When I obtain neutral reactions only for these substances it always appears to indicate a general toxæmic state which precedes or follows treatment in cancer.

CHAPTER IX

SECONDARY TUNING

MY secondary circuit goes up to 111,111 ohms. At present I look for three different sets of tuning—three different factors in the health of the body :—

(1) I ascertain whether the various frequencies indicating glands, presence of micro-organisms, need for drugs, etc., balance at 37 ohms, or at 3,700 ; it is just the same thing.

(2) I then take the general body tuning which should, in the human being = 49,000 positively, negatively and neutrally. Each group in evolution has its own general body tuning. If there is an inflammatory condition positive + and negative − tunings are below normal, and neutrals above normal. General body tuning does not follow the 37 balance rule. The body tuning is up or down. In cancer, positive tuning is up, negative down, and neutrals very much down. The neutral tuning may go up to 90,000 in a very bad case of inflammatory disease but this is rare. Body tuning recovers first, long before individual frequencies are balanced, 49,000 ohms is reached for the body generally, but when this point is reached the patient feels more vitality. In mammals the general body tuning = 38,000 and balance occurs at 35 ohms.

(3) Secondary tuning as indicating comparative intensity is of importance in the diagnosis of sex before birth and of the psychological tendency in some persons ; for mind alters body. Pregnancy can be recognised by tuning to the uterus on 13,360, on the second rheostat, 58,225 tunes to a fœtus ; if these give a reaction above 37 pregnancy has commenced. If the fœtus number will repeat on a series of rheostats the child is alive.

The sex can be recognised during the third month by taking the relative intensities of the testicular 14,999 and ovarian 18,990 frequencies. These relative intensities increase as pregnancy advances.

The 37 balance tells nothing about sex ; this is a health balance for both sets of glands.

A man may be normally formed and perfectly healthy, but the internal secretion for ovarian may nearly equal that for the orchitic. This indicates a mental attitude. Or the case may be reversed ; a woman may have an increased intensity of secretion of testes above normal without being in any way unhealthy bodily or mentally. They may function correctly sexually and have children, but if you know them well there is an attitude of mind to account for the measured reaction.

There are, of course, people who are definitely abnormal who would give an altered balance as in diseased condition. Relative intensities are important for research as I show in the chapter on Glands for showing the relationship between one gland and another.

(4) Sometimes one finds that a patient is balanced as regards bacterial and all other frequencies, but that the normal intensity is below par. For these colour treatment is indicated. The observer must work out the normal intensity for himself; it depends on his apparatus and its setting.

(5) Even though a 49,000 secondary tuning correct in intensity is obtained one must not be satisfied that all is quite correct. There are what I might term pockets of imbalance, and these must be sought for before the patient is reported normal.

PART II

CHAPTER X

ANATOMICAL STUDY

EVERY structure in the body when tested in the circuit has its own particular tuning. If we compare these tunings with those of ordinary wireless the organ vibrations are comparable with the broadcasts from London, Paris or Berlin. Each system, such as the nervous or vascular system, has a wave which is common to every part of it, and each part has its own particular frequency.

A good deal of work has already been done on this subject, but a great amount remains. Hayward, Hardin, Lecoq, McRoberts and Petree have all contributed, and I have done a certain amount of research myself from actual specimens and dissections. I give here the results of my work up to date. What is needed is that some central authority should collect the results from all workers and publish these and, further, subsidise workers to make a complete study of the body. This would be a really useful piece of work, and if properly organised a fairly complete anatomical study could be published a year or two hence.

In diagnosis " locality calls " on structure and organ tunings are very important. Every organ and structure should balance at 37 ohms + and —. For instance, if the appendix measures 37 + and — it is free from disease and there is no need to worry about it. There is, however, another test : supposing that there is a streptococcal infection of the intestines. It is always important to know whether the appendix is infected, in which case it is likely to flare up and involve an operation, whereas if the cæcum only is infected the outlook is quite different. To make this test the particular type of streptococcal frequency is put up on the first rheostat in the primary circuit, and the local call for appendix on the second rheostat. If the appendix is normal the secondary tuning will register 37 ohms + and —. If the appendix is infected the combined wave = 74 +. In this way, by the use of local calls, the actual site of infection can be located. Sometimes an infection or special increase of toxæmia can be traced to a certain part of the patient by going over him with the electrode and it may be found that a certain spot in the nervous system is infected. These tests, together with the symptoms, may suggest certain nerve centres, and by taking a personal rate, after the tuning for the special infection has been placed on the first rheostat, a local call for that particular situation may be obtained.

Some work on nerve centres has been done by visualisation, i.e. concentrating on the idea of the centre and the mechanism it controls. Thought is vibration and causes definite waves. Work on these lines is purely experimental and results obtained by such a method should be severely tested. A good deal, I believe, could be done in this way, but great concentration is needed and most careful checking. Imperfect visualisation will give a frequency which, although present, is not the most important. I mention this method because it may prove to be a basis for getting at nerve centres which could hardly be got at otherwise. This kind of work should be done by independent workers ; if the bulk of them hit on the same frequencies the probability of their usefulness would be considerable.

It is by the foregoing method of localising that organs and structures can be studied from a drop of blood or sputum when the patient is absent. For example, supposing that in a general examination a Morgan infection has been found, the liver should be tested as a possible site of infection. This is done by putting up 97979, the tuning for Morgan, on the first rheostat, and 99834, the tuning for liver, on the second rheostat. If, on measuring, the balance is found to be 37 ohms, it shows that the liver is normal, but if an imbalance is found then the liver is infected by organism or toxin. There is another point which should be noted in connection with this method of localising. Take the case of a patient whose liver has been badly infected, but who is recovering. Morgan will measure 37 in the general circulation, but some trouble may remain locally and can be traced by tuning in as I have just described. In this testing a curious phenomenon sometimes occurs. Supposing no trace of infection has been found when the electrode is placed over the liver, some trouble may be found if the electrode is held over the liver at a distance from the body instead of in direct contact with it. This may be due to the distance magnifying a very small difference in balance or it may indicate that the aura itself has not cleared up. From studies of the aura I believe that either explanation is possible. The aura is just as much a definite structure as our skin. The skin may be infected when the general circulation is clear.

I mention the aura here for two reasons. Firstly, for checking up at a distance to make certain that the balance is really correct, and secondly, because in an anatomical study we must include the aura. Kilner's term for the aura was " The Human Atmosphere," and from this point of view the aura needs investigation.

Organ	Frequency
Æsophagus	46,828
Artery lung	87,770
Arterial system	10,690
Alkaline reserve	67,600
Appendix	15,920
Aorta	43,601
Antrum, Highmore	31,121
Bone	74,533
Breast	77,149
Brain	37,040
Brain, innerside frontal lobes	71,512
Brain, artery	80,437
Brain, olfactory tract	42,631
Brain, cerebellum	93,423
Brain, pons	25,124
Brain, anterior temporo sphenoidal lobe	10,420
Brain, leg motor area	26,325
Brain, arm motor area	31,533
Brain, head motor area	39,003
Brain, third frontal	13,416
Brain, pyramid	35,603
Brain, grey matter, leg, motor area	94,471
Brain, frontal lobes	12,626
Brain, covering membrane	41,390
Brain, grey matter, cerebellum	56,042
Brain, occipital nerve	28,330
Brain, upper corpora quadrigemina	33,040
Brain, lower ditto	50,024
Brain, calamus	84,200
Brain, white matter, cerebellum	30,662
Brain, auditory tubercle	42,425
Brain, auditory nerve	30,475
Brain, facial nerve	84,532
Brain, ocular motor nerve	50,624

Organ	Frequency
Brain, meningeal vein	30,513
Bronchus	35,520
Bile	13,008
Cartilage	84,900
Cæcum	15,980
Colour centre	93,540
Colon, ascending	54,500
Colon, transverse	59,300
Colon, descending	17,875
Clitoris	75,506
Coronary artery	34,624
Duodenum	72,510
Middle ear	13,370
Auditory nerve	30,475
Epididymis	14,781
Eye	41,220
Eye lens	22,141
Aqueous humour	13,834
Ciliary muscle..	24,460
Conjunctiva	33,145
Cornea	24,462
Iris	21,240
Retina	32,540
Sclerotic	25,117
Vitreus humour	65,136
Choroid	93,114
Intra-ocular pressure..	12,800
Endocrines—	
Adrenalin	10,998
Mammary	77,149
Cortex, suprarenal	28,887
Medulla ,,	41,744
Orchitic	14,999
Ovarian	18,990
Parathyroid	40,877
Thyroid	10,129
Posterior pituitary	18,888
Anterior pituitary	79,839
Placenta	98,687

Organ	Frequency	Organ	Frequency
Endocrines—		Nerve, sympathetic ..	73,919
Pancreas	40,115	Nerve, parasympathetic	70,842
Pituitary	26,244	Nerve, olfactory ..	62,230
Whole suprarenal ..	67,091	Nerve, recur. laryngeal	36,101
Thymus ..	13,777	Nerve, vagus ..	67,787
		Nerve, optic	51,290
Frontal sinus ..	77,676	Nail, finger .. · ..	62,450
		Nasal septum ..	74,172
Gall-bladder	39,989	Nerve, facial	84,532
		Nose, superior tur-	
Heart	64,637	binate	60,911
Heart, endocardium ..	98,688	Nose, middle turbinate	59,989
Heart muscle	64,790	Nose, inferior turbinate	67,999
Heart, aortic valve ..	43,502	Nose, ethmoid ..	87,878
Heart, tricuspid valve	61,835		
Heart, mitral valve ..	33,071	Peyer's patch .. · ..	76,988
Heart, pulmonary valve	57,173	Penis	91,155
Heart, right ventricle	62,227	Portal vein	98,889
Heart, left ventricle	62,440	Prostate	41,715
Heart, right auricle ..	31,234	Pleura	82,944
Heart, left auricle ..	21,722		
		Rectum	19,911
Jejunum	50,772		
		Solar plexus ..	70,250
Kidney	31,191	Sex centre A[1] ..	81,424
Knee-joint	39,805	Sex centre B[2] ..	81,524
		Sex centre C[3] ..	66,816
Lung	72,260	Sweat gland ..	97,133
Lymphatic gland ..	30,255	Skin	90,612
Lymph..	83,339	Spleen	83,440
Liver	99,834	Stomach	48,848
Liver, left lobe ..	73,425	Stomach (cardiac end)	30,205
Liver, right lobe ..	54,630	Stomach (pyloric end)	51,240
Liver, caudate lobe ..	35,220		
Liver, quadrate lobe ..	93,040	Teeth	70,269
Liver, portal vein ..	62,251	Tonsils	14,980
Liver, hepatic artery	43,992	Tendons	89,689
Liver, hepatic duct ..	82,442	Toe nail	39,042
Ligaments	18,800	Trachea	36,114
Larynx	16,900	Tongue	43,594
Muscle	59,900	Urethra	27,290
Membrane, synovial ..	39,815	Uterus	13,360
Membrane, mucous ..	62,454		
		Vulva	18,879
Nervous system ..	11,090	Visualization centre ..	82,160
Nerve, supra-orbital ..	46,314	Vena cava, inferior ..	32,668
Nerve, infratroc. ..	65,679	Vein, meningeal ..	30,513

[1] Changes from any cause.
[2] Change or lack of desire.
[3] May indicate excess or masturbation

CHAPTER XI

I.—INTERNAL SECRETIONS

(1) INTRODUCTORY

WHEN I was a student the idea of a gland giving an internal secretion was confined to the ductless glands : the thyroid, parathyroid, adrenals, pituitary, pineal and thymus. Somewhat later it was recognised that the sex glands gave an important internal secretion. It is now becoming recognised that all the glands and organs have internal secretions, and my own work shows me that every structure gives off something to the rest of the body.

Research on the lines started by Abrams shows that every cell is sending off radiations which affect every other cell to a limited extent. This is accepted in the study of the Cosmos by astronomers and what is true in the study of the Cosmos is true in the study of our little bit of it—the human body. Here, however, the general laws of physics are modified by our special form of life, which modifies the vital form of physics which rules us. What makes a study of vital physics so fascinating is the interplay of two great principles : (1) the reign of law which we know must be there, and (2) the reaction of personality to this law. The orthodox school of medicine has, in its physiological and pathological laboratories, made great strides in describing methods of how this and that mechanism works in the body. The Homœopathic school as a whole seems to discard these rules and to regard each patient as a distinct personality. They say, find the similimum for the man as a whole and you have all that is needed. There is truth in this, but unless we study to find general laws we get no further, for in man, and more especially in woman, personality again and again appears to override general laws. Here again we must try to codify experience to enable us to tackle the laws under which personality acts. We must not be deterred by the difficulties ; mistakes we are sure to make, but he who makes no mistakes makes nothing.

Among the many factors which go to form personality we must, on evidence, give a place of great importance to endocrine " make-up." I use this term as it covers either a change in balance or a lowered or increased activity of gland supply.

For example, a person may have sex-gland measuring 37 ohms, i.e. correct health balance, and yet it may be of rather low activity. In persons of a certain type of character I find a corresponding type of secretion. A considerable knowledge of the effects of gland secretions on emotions has already been gained quite apart from wave studies, and a great deal of what follows is merely confirmation of the work of others. Some of these types are well recognised. For instance, instability in temper, the liability to over-emotion of the person with too much thyroid and also the stodginess, placidity and laziness of the myxœdema patient are well known. The latter is often as economical of the truth as the former is ready to give it in excess. An excess of gland-supply of one particular type, for no one gland is ever in excess alone, will colour the whole character and life. We all recognise these characters when we meet them, but we do not all consider that it is due to an over-supply of gland secretion. Take sex for an example. To have too little sex secretion means coldness, perhaps an unhappy marriage and imperfect sympathy, but the greater troubles lie in store for the over-sexed. I remember one case of a woman in charge of a large institution. Her whole mind seemed to be swamped in sex. She claimed to stand for morality, yet she suspected every member of the male and female staff. The minds of others seem equally interested in their digestive powers. A newly-arrived Major in my regiment, when grumbling at my messing arrangements, which satisfied everyone else, frankly said " My belly is my god." It would have been interesting to measure the internal secretion from his stomach ; the external secretion usually met the wonderful strain he put on it.

To what is our endocrine make-up due ? First of all there is heredity. Each parent contributes the condition he or she is in at the time of conception. Then there is environment. Bandler describes how he has found deficient adrenal cortex in children who had been suppressed or frightened by ghost stories, and I have measured the same deficiency in persons who were overshadowed by a vigorous personality, or who dreaded some coming calamity. Food and drinking-water supply will affect the endocrine make-up, and it is well known that thyroid trouble is due to water and soil. Occupation, bad air and lack of sunlight alter secretions and lastly, when infections are present, important changes occur. And here we ask the question : Do infections cause or follow altered conditions of gland supply ? They certainly cause an alteration ; gland make-up may be well-balanced just before an attack

and markedly altered afterwards.   This I have measured.
Further, I think all will agree that organisms successfully
attack those who provide a suitable soil.   This is most
marked in chronic disease, and is illustrated by the following
examples :—

Tubercle affects those who have a poor supply of calcium
and low parathyroid.

The typhoid group more readily affects those who have a
poor chlorine supply and low thryoid.

Cancer affects those who have a poor supply of samarium
and illinium, and of sex gland and parathyroid.

I endeavour here to show :—

(1) The action of glands on each other.
(2) The action of stimuli on glands.

    (a) Emotions.
    (b) Diseases.
    (c) Drugs.

(3) The action of glands on certain body mechanisms.
(4) To discuss how to recognise glands by wave measurements and how each recognition is justified.
(5) To discuss certain special features of gland action.

In the space I can allow myself much must be left out that
has been done by others, and I fully recognise how very imperfect is the small amount which I have been able to do, but
everything must have a beginning.   I have carried on a few
steps the work started by Abrams.   Although I criticise
what he did, I recognize that I should never have started at all
if it had not been for his work.

(2) METHOD OF STUDY

Gland relations in the body are most complicated.   Every
gland acts on all others in greater or less degree, and it is
difficult to separate their influence inside the body.   What
we know about them has been gradually worked out by
observation and experiment.   Observations on diseased glands
may be fallacious, for a tumour or infection may increase
or decrease action at different periods.

In order to study the relationship of glands I first worked
with extracts.   This enabled me to see the tendency of the
gland, but I could not always obtain the same result by
giving a dose, for every person is different and varies at
different periods.   The action of glands outside the body does,
however, give an idea of how they work.   Such laboratory
experiments are not to be taken as final answers, but they add

to our knowledge, and they can be checked up by actual doses in daily work with patients.

Another method of study for checking results is to take a healthy person whose glands measure 37 ohms + and — and then try the effect of putting into the circuit each gland in turn. This is a satisfactory check on experiments made on glands outside the body, and when the two sets of results coincide I am satisfied. When they differ, further tests should be carried out on some other person.

The tables which follow are, in most cases, the results of a number of experiments and, in all, I have had clinical experience to back them up. My study of glands has spread over some eight years, and if I here record results that are different from views expressed in earlier papers, they are probably the result of what I believe are better methods of study. Where differences exist they are probably due to the method of gland recognition. Originally I worked on figures worked out by Abrams and those who followed him. Abrams recognised thyroid on 6 ohms and Dr. Hayward, I think, discovered that 166 ohms was also indicative of thyroid. In Chapter VI I show that 166 corresponds to 6. These numbers are in similar positions on opposite sides of the table. A 6 reaction from thyroid will correspond with 12, the atomic weight of carbon. I think that Abrams hit on an important element in thyroid, and 166 is also an important element, and so is iodine, but to recognise thyroid by means of a frequency due to one element alone is not satisfactory.

Hayward developed a system of taking what he called " personal rates " from patients. This was the frequency of the greatest importance for that patient, and represented something akin to a picture of his whole condition, just as the homœopath seeks to find by judging symptoms the key drug to the whole condition. To take a " personal rate " I place the dried extract of the gland in the testing box and try to find a frequency which is of the highest intensity present. These frequencies are all represented by numbers in ohms in five figures. I test the " personal rates " by the following methods :—

(1) *On and Off Method.*—The tuning number is placed on the rheostat, an electrode is held over the gland extract by a third person and removed at intervals, the operator reports whether reflex is present or not. Care must be taken not to make the movement too quick.

(2) *Fading-out Test.*—The coils connecting the primary and secondary circuits are separated until the reflex disap-

pears, the number under test is then put up on the rheostat. If the number is satisfactory the reflex reappears. Numbers can be compared, the number which reproduces the reflex across the widest gap is the best.

(3) Another test for the best personal rate as representative of a gland is the degree of intensity or activity obtained on the secondary circuit. The best number will give the highest intensity.

(4) A correct recognition number will fit into its place just as does a portion of a jig-saw puzzle. If satisfactory numbers are obtained the results of the test show a mathematical accuracy. For instance, on examining the intensity of positive and negative frequencies from paired glands, equal or opposite polarities are found.

Anterior pituitary gives $86,666+ 34,444-$,
Posterior pituitary gives $34,444+ 86,666-$.
Actual pairs correspond in this way.

In the case of adrenals I had no recognition number for the medulla, and had to use adrenalin for this purpose so that my numbers did not correspond with the reading for cortex of which I had a specimen. However, after a series of experiments I obtained the number 47,144 for medulla.

The figures then worked out thus :—
Adrenal cortex $52,222+ 17,777-$,
Adrenal medulla $17,777+ 52,222-$.
This number for medulla passed the other tests I have described.

The question has been raised by Dr. Boyd of how far one is justified in recognising any gland on a personal rate. He suggests that any impurity might alter the rate obtained. This is quite true if the impurity is gland matter. The investigation was made originally on glands prepared by Parke Davis & Co. and specially supplied for the purpose by the kindness of Dr. Stanley White. Results have been checked up by observation on the living body and from sections.

I think that the difficulty about getting pure specimens of whole glands is not very great. When it is desired to get portions of special principles in glands difficulty certainly arises. Messrs. Parke Davis prepared pitressin, the pressure hormone, and pitocin, the hormone acting on muscle ; they did not profess to secure 100 per cent. purity, but they claimed to get an effective preparation in which they succeeded.

One method of recognising a pure gland is to measure the

positive and negative polarities against its pair. Note the following figures of intensity :—

Gland			Positive	Negative
Testicle	..	..	89,999	19,999
Ovary ..	..	..	19,999	89,999
Thyroid	..	..	25,555	76,666
Parathyroid	..		76,666	25,555
Pitocin	..	..	4,111	36,666
Pitressin	..	..	48,888	5,111

The latter should be a pair if pure, but it is obvious they are not pure—they do not balance.

Experimentally on normal human beings pitocin and pitressin are close enough to purity to effect balanced reactions and clinically they are effective.

In addition to the mathematical proof given above I have found that the highest intensity frequencies worked out from glands, elements, drugs and other structures, are clinically satisfactory and I have been using them for some years.

Another friendly critic suggested that the wave obtained from say dried thyroid would not be the same as that from live thyroid, because dried thyroid had lost water. If the H.I.F. obtained from a preparation was its molecular formula this would be a sound argument. The H.I.F. of any substance is not its molecular or atomic weight. It is something else, invariably different. Every substance I have tested whose molecular weight is known has given me a reaction on its molecular weight, but its H.I.F. gives a still higher intensity.

GLAND POLARITIES.

Gland			Recognition number	Intensities in secondary circuit	
				Positive	Negative
Testicle	..	..	14,999	89,999	19,999
Ovary	..	..	18,990	19,999	89,999
Anterior pituitary		..	79,839	86,666	34,444
Posterior pituitary		..	18,888	34,444	86,666
Thyroid	..	..	10,129	25,555	76,666
Parathyroid		..	40,877	76,666	25,555
Cortex } Adrenals	..	..	28,887	54,444	19,999
Medulla }	..	..	47,144	19,999	54,444
Pineal	..	..	34,939	69,999	28,888
Thymus	..	..	13,777	28,888	69,999
Pitocin*	..	..	96,989	4,111	36,666
Pitressin*	..	..	76,997	48,888	5,111
Red bone-marrow		..	37,860	58,888	23,333
Spleen	..	..	55,556	25,555	86,666
Brain	..	..	17,989	188,888	28,888
Liver	..	..	99,834	18,888	79,999
Adrenalin	..	..	10,998	19,999	49,999

Paired glands and opposed portions of glands give similar figures.
*Manufacturers' products not absolutely pure separation.

The substance flashes out this wave with far greater intensity than any other wave. The H.I.F. is the same from live organism as when dead, and remains the same however much the solution is diluted. It may correspond to the colour-wave seen by clairvoyants.

It is something specific to the nature of the organism or compound ; it is something of great importance but is not altered by death, drying or solution.

So far the recognition of substances by their H.I.F. seems to me quite satisfactory, except that I do not know to what it is due.

The preceding table shows the H.I.F. and polarity intensities of the internal secretory glands,

II.—SPECIAL ACTION OF GLANDS ON CERTAIN MECHANISMS

It is not easy to give anything like a complete picture of the glands, for they are all acting together on the total personality, stimulating and inhibiting each other, and various body processes. When doing experiments to find out how they act, the first thing is to find out the tendencies of each gland.

In a sick person there are so many changes in balance that the action of any gland in that case may not be quite the same as it is in another sick person. For instance, parathyroid will slow down the action of the sex glands in a normal person, but in a person who needs parathyroid beyond all other glands, parathyroid will stimulate all the endocrines. I therefore use a normal person for study of the tendencies of glands. As he has no need of any gland at all, the result of stimulation by any gland is not prejudiced by his condition.

I have found it frequently desirable to give a daily dose of something to assist in maintaining daily and hourly balance. I find, in practice, that a dose of gland-extract is often suitable for this purpose. It seems possible to get results quickly by giving substances which are closely allied to our own, and easy to assimilate. Although these gland-products have to be broken down before they are assimilated into our own tissues, the process of building up again appears to be easier than the formation of gland-tissue from other forms of food.

The radio-active effects of glands can be measured before this breaking-down takes place. Indeed, they can be measured directly the gland has been swallowed. An immediate change takes place, similar to that which can be measured when the gland is merely in the circuit. This effect, as regards intensity, is temporary.

Practically, I have found it useful to stimulate certain body mechanisms with a daily dose of glands ; every doctor has used Pepsin, but possibly he has not realised its effect on blood-pressure.   I give, in this section, a report on certain experiments the results of which have been of practical use and have enabled me to select the correct gland to give to my patients.

The following table gives the effects of the glands on a normal male, normality being 37 ;   an increase indicates stimulation.   The figure after each gland shows the degree of change of balance.

The following table shows the effects of glands and organs on the sympathetic measured on 73,919 ohms and parasympathetic measured on 57,542.   They were also tested on Adrenalin and on Acetyl Choline, and gave exactly comparable results.   Those glands which increased the sympathetic wave lowered the parasympathetic and vice versa Acetyl choline increases 57,542 and reduces 73,919 tested on male.

Stimulators of sympathetic	Stimulators of parasympathetic
Thyroid	Parathyroid
Ovary	Testis
Suprarenal	Pituitary
Adrenalin	Suprarenal cortex
Posterior pituitary	Anterior pituitary
Thymus	Pineal
Liver	Cerebral extract
Spleen	Kidney

The sex glands acted in the opposite way in the female.

My next object of research was to ascertain the effect of glands on blood-pressure.   Work has been done on this subject in other ways, but it seemed desirable to add the evidence of my own method.

It may seem curious that one should be able to do this by taking radio reactions.   The fact that it is possible must be due to the increase or decrease of some substance with high or low blood-pressure.   I must leave for the future the study of the substance I work on.

MacRoberts discovered that blood-pressure could be estimated by working a 450-ohms reaction.   Stranger still, not only can one get an idea about blood-pressure on balance, but if the reaction be measured on ohms the resulting figure gives a very close relationship to the figure obtained with the finger on a Tycho sphygmomanometer.   Further, I checked three readings against an automatic meter which registered

without using the finger.   Also, when 450 registers 37, one
gets an ohm reading which is reasonable for age and condition
It is, undoubtedly, a very fair guide to the pressure.

When 450 ohms is down below 37, pressure is up ; it is, of
course, some substance which varies when the pressure varies.

The following observations were taken on the blood of my
subject, at the time 450 in him was 37 and pressure estimated
in ohms 131.   The figures against each gland show the result.
The figures are, of course, exaggerated by the fact that the
gland was in constant connection with the blood being tested,
and I record the result of the early radio-active effect.

EFFECTS OF GLANDS ON BLOOD-PRESSURE.

Decreased by			Increased by		
Thyroid	..	101	Parathyroid	..	192
Pitocin	..	41	Pitressin	..	182
Cortex	..	130	Adrenalin	..	181
Thymus	..	100	Pineal ..	..	193
Liver	..	111	Brain ..	..	191
Pancreas	..	100	Kidney ..	..	192
Prostate	..	101	Anterior pituitary	..	139
Pepsin	..	41	Posterior pituitary	..	146
Testis	..	121	Spleen	..	191

I have never failed with Elixir Pepsin to get down a blood-
pressure.   Of course the cause must be found and removed,
but Pepsin and Pancreas have both proved useful as a help
in treating high blood-pressure.   Every patient whose blood-
pressure is raised I have found deficient in Pepsin.   Ovarian
extract also tends to raise pressure in the male.   Low blood-
pressure is accompanied by excess of Pepsin in those cases
which I have tested.   Raised blood-pressure seems always to
be connected with intestinal toxæmia, often with a syphilitic
basis, and the use of Pepsin and Pancreas keeps down the
intestinal absorption of inimical organisms.

The next series of experiments were carried out to find out
the effects of glands on acidity, and the alkaline reserve balance.
On consideration I came to the conclusion that the best test
for acidity would be to take readings on 1 ohm representing
the hydrogen atom.   MacRoberts' 676 ohms frequency was
accepted as representing the alkaline reserve, for though I
have no knowledge as to what substance it represents I have
always found that MacRoberts' work was sound.

In the result it will be seen that whether these two frequencies are sound in conception or not they do work together.
The glands were tested on a male who was in a normal state of
health, and in whom 676 ohms and 1 ohm registered 37 +
and −.

Result of introduction of solid glands into testing circuit on a male :—

Solid glands				Acid	Alkaline reserve
Thyroid	..	..	..	34	40
Parathyroid	..	..	..	40	34
Anterior pituitary	..	..		34	40
Pitocin ..	..	..	..	41	35
Pitressin	..	..	..	42	32
Cortex ..	..	..	..	33	41
Adrenalin	..	..	..	42	32
Pineal ..	..	..	.:	34	40
Thymus	..	..	..	40	34
Testis ..	..	..	..	34	40
Ovary ..	..	..	..	40	34
Ovarian residue	..	..		53	21
Bone marrow ..	..	..		32	42
Spleen ..	..	..	..	42	32
Liver extract ..	..	..		33	41
Cerebral extract	..	..		41	33

Ovarian residue had the opposite effect on a normal female, and increased alkaline reserve to a greater extent than any other gland. It might well be used in women before an operation or after if there are signs of acidosis. Possibly intersticial tissue from the testis would be suitable in men. In its absence Cortex and bone marrow are indicated for men. It will be noted that the glands which increase the alkaline reserve most are bone marrow, Pitressin, Thyroid, sex-gland and Pineal.

The next experiments were tried to find out the relative action of gland extracts in an increase of oxydation. The test was taken on 8 ohms for oxygen. Any gland that raises oxydation will probably increase the temperature and increase the rate of metabolism generally. The test was made on normal persons whose 8 ohm or oxygen atomic number reactions measured 37 ohms. Higher figures than this show an increase in oxygen activity. The figures used are those of the balance reactions. They simply show the tendency and the comparative effect in raising and lowering the function of oxidation.

ACTION OF GLANDS ON OXYGEN

Where not otherwise stated results are recorded on male, whose oxygen reaction was 37.

Adrenalin is probably rather more active than medulla, which accounts for the variation shown above ; paired glands usually match each other in the intensity of their effects.

Increase by	Positive	Decrease by	Negative
Pineal	52	Thymus	52
Adrenal cortex ..	54	Adrenalin	56
Brain	50	Liver	50
Thyroid	46	Parathyroid	46
Posterior pituitary ..	60	Anterior pituitary ..	60
Pancreas	52	Kidney	61
Bone marrow	51	Spleen	51
Mammary	50	On female mammary ..	60
Orchitic	60	On female orchitic ..	60
On female ovarian ..	60	On male ovarian ..	60
On female placenta ..	70	On male placenta ..	70

The effects of using the opposite sex-gland are interesting. The more experience I get in testing the effect of sex-glands the more I am convinced of the importance of balancing both sides of the sex system. Persons may be normal on their own sex-gland but minus on the opposite sex-gland ; they may be a bit plus on their own, very markedly down on the opposite sex-gland. When this is the case the opposite sex-gland will suit them very well, lowering to normal the sex-gland proper and raising the energy of heart or liver or any organ that is below par. Ovarian in men is as good as orchitic in women for increasing function where it is needed and lowering it where needed. Those who live too fast and are nervy, especially those who masturbate, need the opposite sex gland. My friend, Dr. Temple Silvester, has had good results among lunatics who masturbate by using Ovarian extract on men. He used a high dilution made on allopathic methods. My experience is that these cases need the solid or at most a 3x or 1 in a 1,000 solution.

The good result must be due not only to levelling up gland supply, but to soothing the nervous system, of which lowering oxidation is merely one sign.

These results confirm what I have laid stress on elsewhere, that the Thymus and Parathyroid are glands which lower activity and act as controls. They are glands to be given to those who are living too fast and to the over-sexed. The action of liver in lowering oxygen metabolism may be what is needed in some anæmia cases, but its action in this direction should be watched and balanced if need be.

Another investigation made was an attempt to see if we could find which glands would have the best effect in antagonising micro-organisms. I put a collection of these, some thirty to forty, in the circuit, got a combined wave and then tested out the glands in turn. The result was that Pancreas was top of the list and Parathyroid second. I did not test out the salivary glands, but it is possible that these may be active in this way. The Pancreas was certainly more active than Pepsin.

There are, of course, obvious criticisms to make on this procedure, and those who have not worked by means of radio-active tests may hardly see the importance of the test. It does not mean that Pancreas will suit every case of infection, but it does suit a number of cases where one would not have expected to have to give Pancreas. It is especially suitable for tubercular infections. I give the glands in order of effectiveness in reducing the wave 82,350 with an intensity of 72,222 ohms produced by our mixed bag of bacilli and cocci of very varied kinds, including perhaps a preponderance of bowel organisms. The figures against the glands indicate the intensity to which they reduced the 72,222 intensity registered when they were absent.

EFFECTIVENESS OF GLANDS IN REDUCING ACTIVITY OF ORGANISMS.

1. Pancreas	..	..	..	48
2. Parathyroid	..	..	..	1,555
3. Thyroid	..	..	..	1,777
4. Cortex	..	..	..	7,333
5. Placenta	..	..	..	14,444
6. Thymus	..	..	..	14,444
7. Pituitary	..	..	..	14,444
8. Ovarian residue	..	..	34,444
9. Post pituitary	..	..	34,444
10. Ovarian extract	..	..	37,777
11. Mammary	..	..	..	39,999
12. Orchitic extract	..	..	49,999
13. Prostate	..	..	..	62,222
14. Cerebral extract	..	..	63,333

EFFECTS OF EMOTIONS ON MALE GLANDS.

	Courage	Rage	Fear	Enthusiasm	Pity	Sex excitement	Philanthropy	Joy
Adrenals, medulla	+14	+24	−7	+13	−2	+24	=7	+23
Adrenals, cortex	+15	+25	−7	+13	−8	+28	+7	+23
Orchitic	+17	−5	−2	+13	−8	+37	+8	+28
Thyroid	−8	+3	normal	+2	+3	+13	+13	+13
Parathyroid	+13	+3	+20	+2	+4	−13	−13	+ 8
Anterior pituitary	+4	−6	−4	+2	n'mal	n'mal	+15	+ 1
Pitocin	+1	+13	−14	−2	+13	−10	n'mal	+ 8
Pitressin	−1	−13	+14	+2	−13	+10	n'mal	+ 8
Pineal	+14	−10	−20	+13	+24	−10	+29	+17
Thymus	−14	+10	+20	−13	−24	+10	−29	−17

The figures indicate the amount of positive secretion above or below normal reaction, 37 ohms.

These researches have proved of practical use in my work. I do not use any gland preparation unless it works into my prescription made out on the auric frequencies which are representative of the whole man. The suggestions gained do, however, shorten my work in finding out what is most beneficial. People who are too fat fail in oxidation and the glands which increase oxidation are suitable for reducing fat. That is one or more of them is likely to be found useful for the purpose.

III.—INTERNAL SECRETIONS AND EMOTIONS

The foregoing table shows the effects of emotion on glands, or we had better say the tendency of emotion towards the glands. If one could register the effect of real genuine passion or fear the result would be more striking. They were obtained thus : the emotion was acted, and while this was being done appropriate sentences were written on paper.

Writing gives a permanent record of the condition of the writer at the time if his fingers are moist enough, and we can therefore at leisure check up the gland effects. This is fortunate as it would be difficult to keep on acting an emotion while a number of tests were made.

I sometimes hear it said, " I can understand a blood specimen giving information ; I can't believe writing does." Yet cases are always being reported of clairvoyance from handwriting, notably an experiment with Einstein's handwriting lately. Further, there is a regular science of the study of handwriting.

Handwriting conveys much to different experts, and sometimes it is a better indication even than blood for my purposes. I have frequently checked-up writing and serum side by side.

I had a letter from a lady describing a nightmare which worried her at intervals. The remedy for this in her case was usually aconite. We got the indication for aconite from her signature page, and when we tested the place in the letter where she had spoken of the nightmare the indication was many times stronger, and the cortex of the adrenal was markedly lowered, especially in the frontal part of the brain.

One can localise on the subject from a letter just as well as one can from blood. It is fairly easy to understand why a letter should convey frequencies from the person writing it. To begin with, they are touching the paper usually with both hands, and one hand is moving over the paper ; in some ways writing under these conditions is a better indication of momentary conditions than blood or serum from the mouth. There may be something more subtle than hand-touch and movement of pen, at any rate altered conditions in chemistry and waves can be conveyed in writing.

Nature is much more marvellous than we can imagine, but it is best perhaps at first to be content with the simplest explanation, with the mental reservation that the Dame has something much more complex in reserve and I am always suspicious of simplicity in scientific explanation.

In the emotion I have termed " philanthropy " I thought not only of a desire to help others, but of work done and doing for others. This resulted in increased pineal, sex-gland, thyroid and anterior pituitary. Bandler suggests a good secretion of anterior pituitary is connected with good and firm character ; it is curious it only came out really strong in this connection. Clinically I agree with Bandler.

In " joy " I thought of the enjoyment of fine weather in open country, successes in work, joy in family life and in all human affairs. Here we have a considerable increase in sex-gland and less pineal than in the wider view of philanthropy.

In both there was some feeling of creative work. For that, a good positive secretion of the creative gland is needed. In sex excitement naturally the internal secretion of the sex-gland is high, and also the adrenals, the relation of cortex to sex-gland being particularly close, the anterior pituitary, an essentially male gland, does not share the stimulus, it being mainly connected with secondary sex characters such as frame and distribution of hair.

Of all the emotions tested fear has the most depressing effects on the positive secretions. If one could register during a real genuine fear, with hair on end and creepy skin, positive secretions would almost disappear and also pineal, which appears to be the most affected. It is curious that the thyroid was not more affected. However, one has merely to record results and the experiment shows tendencies. The fear thought of was psychological not physical.

The sex-gland results are interesting. Every expansive idea increases the sex internal secretion ; in pity it is diminished, and this is, in a sense, an expansive idea, being concerned with the troubles of others—but pity *per se* is a futile sort of emotion, it is only when pity is combined with action that it is of any real use. With action the other emotions come into play that would cause an expansive action of the glands. Pity is a kind of fear for others.

The thyroid shares the increase and is, as usual, markedly affected in all emotions.

The most striking fact in the series is the effects on pineal and thymus. They are always balanced one against the other, always considerably affected—markedly in all emotions of an unselfish kind. Rage, fear and sex-excitement lower pineal. One feels that everything that increases self-regard reduces this gland; it must decrease considerably in the miser.

Obviously, if you want a good generous gland secretion, interest yourself in others, have wide sympathies—expand your personality. My feeling is that a person with extra pineal occupies a larger space in the world. It does actually expand the aura, sometimes by several feet, when needed.

If you live for your immediate surroundings you contract; if you live for yourself alone you are in danger of ultimate breakdown. Probably anyone who reads this book realises that our personality spreads considerably beyond our skins. Kilner could demonstrate our auras for a few inches, but powerful personality, particularly if unpleasant, can pervade a house. Literally you can feel it on opening the door. I remember a hardy Australian soldier, an outdoor man, pointing this out to me. Not a man you would expect to be sensitive. I have known hate to be so violently offensive that it made me feel sick and gave a sense of bad smell. Both I and others fled from the room and aired it before returning. I have known those who have to live with this sort of thing fade in health; sex-gland secretion and pineal dropped to a dangerously low ebb.

It is ridiculous that people who excite each other in this way should be expected to live together, it is bad for all parties concerned; such an atmosphere is dangerous to health. Instead of trying to patch up the peace where real hatred is mutual, the parties should be separated promptly, even if it is mainly one-sided; the injury to health is considerable.

Prolonged continued bad thinking produces an atmosphere. Kipling's tale " The House Surgeon " is true to fact. Probably many ghost stories are simply due to the mind impressions on the atmosphere by strong emotions, recognised by those sensitive to such impressions. There is no proof the poor souls who underwent the experience remain locally; it is more likely that merely their thoughts have remained.

Thought is all-important, far more important than acts; thoughts may lead to acts, and are in a sense indestructible.

IV.—THE SEX GLANDS

The gland which makes more difference to you than anything else is your sex-gland. The first question asked about you is : " Is it a boy or a girl, doctor ? " According to the development of certain cells in the embryo the fate of the future personality is decided. If the male type predominates you get glands of a certain type, if female quite a different type. Social activities of various kinds, from games to politics, may be shared by both sexes ; the social barriers between the sexes are being broken down. Women are taking a larger part in the world's affairs, but so long as human nature remains the types will remain distinct, physically and mentally. It is not only the ovary and testicle that separate women from men, but the other glands are differently constituted in the two sexes.

Those who have not dabbled in wireless are unable to think in terms of frequencies, so I will put it this way : the female thyroid has a far closer connection with the ovary than the male thyroid has with the testes ; the female thyroid appears to be open to attack in certain conditions when the male thyroid is resistant. Clinical observations correspond with the measured connection given in the following table, and the fact that Ovarian extract has a far greater effect on thyroid than Testicular extract has. The cortex or outer part of the adrenal gland, has a close connection with the testis and increases testicular activity far more than it does ovarian. The Anterior Pituitary also affects the male sex-gland more than the female sex-gland, whereas the Posterior Pituitary affects the female sex-gland more than the male (*see* figs. in table).

RELATION OF THE SEX-GLANDS.

Electrode placed over gland being tested.

1st RHEOSTAT Figures in ohm representing			MALE Figure on 2nd rheostat representing	Activity in ohms	FEMALE 2nd rheostat	Activity in ohms
Thyroid	..	..	.. Testicle	13,333	Ovary	38,888
Parathyroid	..		,,	74,444	,,	62,222
Posterior pituitary	..		,,	9,444	,,	74,444
Anterior pituitary	..		,,	78,888	,,	9.333
Cortex	..	..	.. ,,	77,777	,,	17,777
Medulla	..	..	.. ,,	35,555	,,	73,333
Muscle ..	..	..	.. ,,	33,333	,,	27,777
Pineal	..	..	.. ,,	47,777	,,	52,222
Thymus	..	..	.. ,,	47,777	,,	52,222
Liver	..	..	.. ,,	18,888	,,	23.333
Brain	..	..	.. ,,	23,333	,,	24,444
Bone-marrow	..	..	,,	56,666	,,	43,333
Spleen	..	..	.. ,,	25,555	,,	31,111

What has been measured is the testicular or ovarian factor in each gland in the list.

We can test these relationships in another way. The substance to be tested is placed in the dynamiser and then each gland is introduced into the circuit. By this method we get the following results :—

WITH TESTICLE IN THE DYNAMISER :—

Marked increase by adding	Some increase	Decrease
Pineal	Adrenal (whole)	Parathyroid
Cortex	Thyroid	Posterior pituitary
Ovary		Adrenalin
Anterior pituitary		

WITH OVARY IN THE DYNAMISER :—

Pineal	Adrenal (whole)	Anterior pituitary
Testicle	Adrenalin	Parathyroid
Thyroid	Cortex	
Posterior pituitary		

I am far from taking the Freudian view that everything is based on sex. I should say that the average English man or woman has a vast number of other sides from which disease can attack him or her. All the same, I notice that sex-glands come to the fore in a larger degree when one can analyse things by measurement than they did before, when one practised on such symptoms as the patient chose or was able to reveal. A lot of trouble comes from a wrong attitude of mind towards sex and its affairs. The rising generation is more sensible than previous ones. A number of women in my generation and the one before were brought up in complete ignorance. The shock of sexual connection spoilt their sexual lives. I have come across such cases and have heard of many others. In spite of one side of the mind being perfectly rational on the subject the other was knocked out of gear, more or less permanently, and reflexes did not function properly. The horror remained still something of a horror. The basis of this was in the mind. The strain on the nervous system was tremendous and in some cases caused very serious nervous symptoms, threatening complete breakdown. Rational talks and endocrine therapy helped and the worst features of the case were relieved, but the original horror remained. I am not so certain as I was that even this sort of mental complex cannot be resolved if we work on the sex centres in the brain ; once the situation has been faced mental conceptions can be turned into frequencies and these balanced. Any gland which is insufficiently active can be stimulated to activity and unbalanced frequencies on the sex centre can be balanced.

Excessive desire may be due to an infection of the genital tract and can be relieved by tackling that. No patient can be helped who does not want to be helped ; if they do, the cause can be worked out and dealt with. Trouble of this kind is largely affected by the mental outlook. There are oversexed people who are rather proud of it and would not want the cause removed. These, of course, will not become patients for this reason, and should they do so for other reasons they cannot be helped unless they become convinced that the condition must be altered. There are those who take a rational view, that sex affairs physically are simply a physiological natural business, and that if things are out of balance they can be dealt with on medical lines just as regulation of the bowels. These people are fairly easy to help. Then there are those who regard over-action of a natural function as sin. This idea must be eradicated. This sort of thing in some cases leads to an asylum and in others to suicide. Some good folks will see in this view a lightness of mind towards sin. I say that the spirit exists in other spheres than the sex organs, and if you pull it down there then you get into trouble. The difficulties of the flesh can be met by other means and the more idealistic the spirit the worse the trouble when you connect it with lower centres of being. I do not say that sexual love cannot be linked to something much higher and more beautiful ; it certainly can. To become perfect we must live fully and healthily in all spheres. Live natural lives sexually and spiritually, denying the just claims of neither the world of the spirit nor of the senses.

Now what can we do for the unbalanced sex organs and centres ? First of all we must examine for toxins and deal with them. I have worked out three waves on the sex centre of the brain, A, B and C, which have certain connections, but which, of course, may relate to a far wider connection. Their unbalance may be due to a number of causes ; this we shall find out in time.

A. 81,424.—This is unbalanced when there is over or under activity of the sex-glands due to any cause.

B. 81,524.—This appears in positive excess cases where there is unsatisfied desire ; when the negative waves are in excess there is, in some cases, frigidity.

C. 66,816.—This is unbalanced and the negative wave increased when there is exhaustion due to sexual excess, but it possibly may be altered from some other cause.

These frequencies need further study. but they are a help when examining the sex system. They should be measured from the sex centre of the brain, about an inch and a half in front of the ear on the eye level. To balance these centres try the effect of Murex, Dirca, Xanthoxyllum, Mentha Pulegium and Chelidonium. When people are older than they should be, the sex-gland is deficient. Failing hearts often benefit from sex-gland treatment. So long as we are secreting a sufficient amount of sex hormone we keep young and cannot get cancer. A sufficiency of sex hormone is needed for creative work of any kind. Our mental reactions towards sex are due to the balance of sex cells.

Normal Sex Balance.—The embryo possesses sets of cells which can form male organs or female organs. In the male there are left some remains of the female organs, part of the Wolffian body and parts of the Mullerian duct, the lower portion of which forms the uterus masculinis in the prostate. Both these give an ovarian wave.

In the ovary there is a portion termed the parovarian which gives a frequency 14,999, i.e. that of the testicle. In the normal individual male and female, the ovarian and testicular frequencies both balance on 37 ohms + the normal balance for all frequencies. This means that a normal female has correct ovarian and parovarian secretion.

By balance measurements therefore, we could not tell male from female. What we have to go on is intensity of the male and female frequency.

A male in full activity should have approximately an intensity for positive testicular secretion on 14,999 ohms = 133,333 ohms and negative = 32,222 ; his ovarian reaction should be 32,222 = 93,333. In the female these figures should be reversed.

Dr. M. C. Hardin of Atlanta, U.S.A., made a special study of this question of male and female balance in individuals. We sat up till 3 a.m. talking it over when I saw him in Chicago in 1928. Hardin told me a most interesting story of his research on this subject. A patient whose reactions to the opposite sex were abnormal consulted him with a view to being treated. Hardin's patient wished to become a normal citizen and have normal sex attractions. After a considerable amount of research Hardin was able to effect this. Soon after he started his research he came across two soldiers with head wounds on the site I have described as the sex area. Hardin was not aware of this connection at that time. The condition of the two men led to the discovery of the sex centre in the brain. In one the bone was broken and there had been a depressed fracture ; this man was completely impotent. In

the other there had been a much slighter injury and this man
had continual irritation of the organs. Hardin then found
that the sex organs could be stimulated or inhibited by
action in this area.

During the course of his studies he found that everyone has
certain degrees of male and femaleness due to gland supply.
The results varied from anatomical changes to a mere masculinity in women or femininity in men not affecting their normal
reproductive powers or sex attractions. In some individuals,
though normally formed, there was such an excess of the
opposite sex-gland beyond normal that ordinary sex attraction
was reversed. Such persons have been termed the third sex.
Pleas have been made for sympathy with these abnormal
persons, even for license for abnormal sex relations. An
individual with an abnormal gland-supply may, of course, be
a perfectly normal person and he or she may be an extraordinarily fine character, but I doubt if the world as constituted
has much use for asexual or bisexual individuals. My own
view is that normality is what is most needed for health,
mentally and bodily.

Hardin has been able to alter these balances, and I feel
sure I could do the same from my experience in balancing gland-
supply, but one essential thing is the desire of the patient
to be normal. I have changed people who were deficient
sexually or oversexed, but they had an earnest desire for the
result I aimed at.

There are, of course, plenty of perfectly healthy people
married, with children, who have an extra amount of femininity
or masculinity. Women recognise the fact in a flash. In
some cases I have been able to follow up such flashes and have
secured measurements which showed that what a woman felt
instinctively was correct.

My observation is that the somewhat feminine man is
attracted by a woman with some masculinity of character.
This character need in no way be shown by the bony and
muscular frame. Some athletic men have feminine traits of
character, some women with great feminine charm of form
have minds very like men. To be able to really sympathise
and deal successfully with both sexes one must have an adequate supply of both secretions.

This question of sex balance, even within healthy limits
does, when health is upset, have an effect on health and may
determine the site of a lesion. A man with an increase of
feminine supply is liable to get the female portions of the
epididymis affected, or a woman the parovarian. Again,

since the total endocrine supply must balance positively and negatively in all healthy individuals if an increase in positiveness or negativeness varies from normal in any gland, compensation must occur elsewhere, either thyroid, adrenals or one portion of the pituitary ; such changes will affect the skin, hair, bones and muscles. More especially do such changes affect character, temper and general bearing towards the world in general.

I remember well a rowing Blue who proved too mild for some of the billets he occupied. He was known as " The Lamb," and his wife as " Mint Sauce " ; both charming and able people, but a little interchange of gland secretions would have saved some troubles.

It appears that we are the creatures our gland-supplies make us. A shock may alter our supply, environment has great influence, poisons from food, bowel absorption, all influence these terminals of the nervous system ; heredity also plays its part. We appear to be the result of forces beyond our control.

Thought alters our gland balances (see section on experiments on emotion on gland supply).

Is personality really due to gland-supply or is gland-supply due to personality ? Are there male and female souls and do these determine sex ? Is the spirit within the deciding factor, not only in sex but in all the gland characteristics that make up the soil of the body that go with character ? Measurements fail us here except that they can show the power of thought. We all know however, all history shows us that a great spirit may triumph over all physical difficulties. So the body may have many unsuitable secondary sex characters due to gland-supply, but the spirit within be that of a truly womanly soul, or the body be feminine in appearance but the spirit may be a leader of men.

Is there any evidence to show how sex is regulated ?

An American researcher working on lines similar to Abrams found that women developed an ovum one month which would produce a male and the next month a female. This may possibly be the case with a large number of women, but the father probably has also something to say in the matter. A friend of mine who runs a poultry farm gets a vast majority of pullet eggs. An experienced breeder told him that he must have that rare bird—a pullet-getting cock. If in poultry a certain male fertilises female ova only, the same may be the case with humans. Probably the same phenomenon occurs in some women. In most families boys and girls occur,

but either parent may have a predominance for creating one
sex only.   To produce both sexes both parents must have
certain elements in the germ cells.   Opposite polarity bodies
of both kinds must be present for fertilisation for either sex.
Femaleness in the father's spermatozoa must meet some
opposite polarity body to become effective.

To be fertile, two opposite polarity forces must meet in the
germ cells.   This question could be settled probably by
poultry and animal breeders if they took the trouble, and
sperm and ova could be examined by the method I use.

In the East the woman who bears sons only gets great
honour.   In Shakespearian England the same view was held.
Henry Vth's Kate scorned to bear aught but men children.

Popular ideas on procreation are, however, not fair to the
lady.

I remember a mother of triplets from dockland saying that
on return home this meant a bashing as well as a thrashing ;
twins, apparently, meant a thrashing only.   Further inquiry
on the subject led to the information that the males of that
region were not merely expressing irritation at an unwanted
addition to their cares, but viewed the double birth as a sign
of unfaithfulness.   I told this tale in a P. & O. smoking room,
and said, " This is particularly bad luck for the ladies, as
there is some evidence of male responsibility for twins."   This
elicited a horrified remark from an engaged man : " Don't
suggest I have this awful power.   My brother's wife has just
had twins."

Experiments to secure male or female children by feeding
up one parent and under-feeding the other, have always
proved useless in the long run.   It is probable that if the
powers of parents can vary, the cause of the preponderance
of male or female births is due to something more subtle than
mere feeding up.   We may be able to find out this secret of
Nature, but that Dame keeps the balance.   The preponderance
of male births after the War is a case in point.

If feeding was the secret the men who had been fighting
were better fed than the women who remained at home, and
this, according to the theory, should have secured a preponderance of daughters.   Schopenhauer talks of " the will of
the child to be " as bringing the sexes together.   Does the
need for male souls to enter the world cause male births ?
I propounded this question in an after-dinner discussion.   In
answer, my friend, Noel Jaquin showed me a hand-impression
with complete double heart, or sex lines, but with one head
or individuality line.   This was taken from an individual—

a South American—who was said to have both male and female organs, and no one could tell which sex predominated. This was the only case Jaquin had seen in fourteen years' study, but he had seen a number of double head-lines which went with alternating personalities.

Diagnosis by the hand lines is just as possible, up to a point, as diagnosis by the iris or retina. All cell-changes cause stigmata all over the body, which can be read if we study them.

Abrams studied this question of causation of sex, and endeavoured to control it by the use of colours. I see no reason why it should not be studied and the knowledge gained used, but there are probably factors which will make it extremely difficult to carry out. Reversion to the bee stage is unlikely. A predominantly male or female population would spell destruction of the race.

Physicians who have to deal with men and women recognise there is something which is clearly outside anatomy and physiology which has to be recognised and dealt with. It is the absolutely different psyche in the sexes which makes our work so fascinating and difficult, from the mechanical medicine point of view. If mechanics are a help they fail unless some small understanding and much sympathy for the opposite sex goes with them.

Modern women may compete with men in games and business, but they are, to men, as incalculable as ever. The world would be a dull place if this ever ceased to be so.

When examining for sex-gland activity, measure up the intensity and balance of both glands in either sex. In some cases it is the opposite sex-gland which is required both in men and women. This is more likely in the case of persons who are not married, or those who are separated physically from their partners.

Before leaving this subject I must say a few words about education. The subject should not be hidden but there is no need to force it on young children under puberty. A girl's first period should not be allowed to arrive quite unexpectedly, that may be a shock. A general outline of physiology should be given to all children over twelve, sex included. Girls should not be allowed to marry in partial ignorance of married life. I have known women who realised that it took two people to make a child but who did not know that marriage connoted sexual intercourse as a matter of course ; the result was a certain degree of shock. I have known cases of practically complete ignorance where the whole life was spoilt and though the union resulted in children, severe nervous trouble resulted, threatening suicide or complete mental breakdown. These cases will be fewer in the future, the modern tendency is to make too much fuss about sex, which is just as bad. The correct attitude is that it is just an everyday matter, a natural urge, like eating when you are hungry and should be controlled on the same lines. Spirituality comes into everything, but it has its dangers as well as the flesh.

There is another subject which must be dealt with in this connection : contraception. This is being discussed by Church and laity and medical people, often with some heat. On the one hand most married couples cannot afford unlimited families and few women can stand perpetual child-bearing. Therefore, by one means or another, limitation is necessary. The extreme party on one side urge practical celibacy when children are not wanted. This may be an ideal but it is not practical for persons sharing one bed, and if an attempt is made to carry it out it is likely to lead to estrangement unless both parties are in thorough agreement. During natural sexual intercourse an exchange of secretions takes place, which means not merely the possibility of spermatozoa reaching an ovum, but of a sex hormone affecting the whole system. Persons who have become used to a natural married life may suffer when deprived of this exchange. I have evidence of this and have been able to modify the effects by giving the opposite sex-gland, but this is only a part of the secretion exchange. When Nature is interfered with she is apt to retaliate ; any method used, therefore, should interfere with natural exchange as little as possible. I advise young people when they ask my advice on this subject to postpone interference as late as possible and then to use methods which do not prevent a natural exchange of hormones. Interference with a delicate mechanism in early married life may prevent children ever arriving and may lead to estrangement or bad health.

Life is a series of compromises ; the wise accept this. Marriage is a matter of give and take. Consideration, tenderness, forethought and humour are needed to make a success. If we are too high up in the clouds a bad drop is likely to occur, if we live too much on the earth we can never soar to a plane more lovely than our present surroundings. It should be possible where love dwells to be kindly, practical and have spiritual union at the same time.

Excess of sex-gland secretion may lead to masturbation. In every case I have found the sex centre vibration in the brain affected ; this can be measured on a spot just behind; the eye and above the zygoma. Most cases also show infection of the sex organs. Circumcision is sound, but mutilating operations which are sometimes performed on girls are really a disgraceful proceeding showing that the operator is entirely ignorant of the causes of the trouble, which are partly due to psychological causes and partly due to bacterial infections. Dirca, calladium, staphysagria and other drugs with psychological treatment and often colour treatment are what is needed.

In sex matters, as in all others, we must be guided by our highest vision, but unless we have natural healthy views such vision may lead to shipwreck.

The cause of sexual union between man and woman should be mutual love and desire for the closest union physically, emotionally, mentally and, I would even add, spiritually. Few can rise up so far at any time, but at any rate it should be happy and natural.

Let the narrowness of asceticism and foul-minded prudery be abolished and let us realise that all pure joy of any sort is worthy of the Creator, and let us try to think on these lines. Life has its compromises, but avoid them till you have to face them, and cast out fear, the spoiler of joy and all the sweet poetry of life.

V.—PINEAL AND THYMUS

The pineal gland has been neglected. It appears to be very little used and information in regard to its function seems to be confined to the statement that it affects growth in the young. In a form of lizard, whose immediate ancestors are supposed to have lived amphibian lives, the pineal was an eye of a kind ; the eye in actual use was not found, but sufficient remains were found in existing lizards to show what the degenerate organ had been.

Occultists regard the pineal as playing an important part in the apparatus of clairvoyance. I have measured this and the pineal is increased in intensity during clairvoyance. What I have found is that the mental states which are outgoing and tend to expand our consciousness towards others increase the activity of the positive pineal, whereas self-regarding states diminish it. The thymus is affected in the opposite direction.

The pineal and thymus are extremely important glands as regards growth ; dwarfs lack pineal and have an excess of thymus. It is a mistake to think that the thymus gland disappears and does not function after puberty ; it functions throughout life, and at all ages balances at 37 + and − in health. In some cases pineal and thymus swing regularly together, like the old man and woman in the toy we used to have as a weather predictor ; the old man came out when it rained and the lady in fine weather. If we allow a sex simile the pineal is the husband and thymus the wife, for the pineal stimulates all the positive frequencies in glands and the thymus the negative.

When there is a general sub-endocrine condition give Pineal, but when there is over-activity give Thymus. When it is possible to measure glandular activity there is no difficulty about prescribing gland extracts, the extracts can be placed in the circuit and results measured. Before any gland is prescribed its effect on general body tuning, disease waves, and biomorphs should be tested, as well as on the particular gland condition which has suggested its use. Pineal and Thymus are especially active in youth and, therefore, we must think of them as youth-restorers and consider their use when there are signs of premature old age. It is often better to use Pineal than Thyroid when sub-thyroid signs are present, as the Pineal is a more general tuner-up. Pineal and Thymus both have the effect, when they are correctly prescribed, of raising under-functioning glands and lowering the action of the over-functioning. Bandler states that Thymus is most helpful in menorrhagia, due to over-activity of the ovary. He agrees with what I have found on measurement, that over-precocious children have too little thymus action. Over-activity of the pineal seems commoner in boys and it is accompanied by over-activity of the testicular internal secretion. When there is a too great anxiety about lessons, masturbation or signs of too great mental activity or of bodily growth for age, Thymus is suggested as a corrective. When the general picture is one of precocity in growth or mind, or too great concentration give Thymus, for this condition means an over-active pineal. Thymus is the steadying gland. Some cases of nettlerash, due to over-production of pepsin and acid, do well on Thymus.

Restlessness may be due to two different conditions : an over-supply of pineal will lead to great activity, a great deal of work will be done and insufficient rest will be taken which may ultimately lead to a breakdown, but the activity is an extension of normal activity and work is accomplished and enjoyed. The difficulty such people have is to switch off ; they are driven by an over-stimulated nervous system. The sub-pineal type is different ; they are unable to rest, not because they enjoy activity and have to do something or explode, but because they are uncomfortable resting and movement lets off a feeling of irritation. Work is not enjoyed and there is heavy weather in its performance or in superintending the work of others. The result of their activity is not commensurate with the output of nervous energy which it apparently entails. Many of us know something of this condition when recovering from severe illness. We know we ought to rest and when we try to work we accomplish very little. Have you ever tried to pack up house and move after being ill ? How many unnecessary movements are made ? To superintend a number of people working for you is almost equally exhausting. Over-pineal restlessness can be met by switching over from one subject to another, sub-pineal restlessness is exhausting in every kind of activity.

Another guide to treatment with these glands is the mental attitude of the patient, concentration on personal affairs, and inclination to too much self-analysis and a too-narrow view of life generally suggest the administration of Pineal. Environment will help to produce these conditions as well as a natural tendency ; women for generations have been the home-birds. It is generally the woman who has to give her attention to a narrower circle of duties, willy nilly, and this has, of necessity, produced a narrower outlook. Pineal, however is very often a useful remedy for men who show signs of premature old age. It should be given in one-tenth gr. doses every other day. In mental exhaustion from over-work it is useful for a very short period for men who are usually well supplied but who are temporarily run down in gland supply. One-tenth gr. should not be exceeded. I have known one-fifth gr. produce a severe headache. In prescribing one should keep in mind mental characteristics, but a patient is not always the same. The over-use of faculties will produce a condition which requires the temporary use of a remedy not indicated by general characteristics. A man who is usually very active-minded on widespread interests may be exhausted, and benefit by a slight rest, plus pineal one-tenth gr., three days a week for two weeks. Do not give him a longer course unless there are chronic signs of breakdown.

Gland treatment alone is useful, but it will not by itself remove causes. It can be a potent stimulant. The baby with the too-patent fontanelle that will not grow needs pineal and thrives on it, as well as the prematurely old. In the case of the infant, one-tenth gr. should be given daily.

Pineal and Thymus, of course, work together in harmony

in the healthy; it is only in the unbalanced that they are apparently at cross-purposes.

I have alluded to the use of Thymus in menorrhagia. Its value appears to depend on its effect in lowering ovarian over-activity. Thymus should be given in cases where there is general over-activity of the metabolism and where any gland is over-active. I do not know whether it has been tried in epilepsy, but it might be of service in cases not due to injury, as it tends to lower cerebral activity. No gland can remove diseased conditions, but it may be of great assistance if correctly used.

In one case of the Mongolian type of bodily and mental deficiency I found marked deficiency of thymus. The case improved under a steady course of Thymus in conjunction with other treatment. I have seen a good deal of " Mongols " and got the impression that they were very different from other types of deficient development. The dwarf usually has an active mental development. The so-called " village idiot ' of the Mongolian type is the more deficient because he has not been trained. Mongols in the richer classes often develop considerable mental powers in some direction, such as music or mechanics. When I had the opportunity of studying them clinically I had but little opportunity for measuring, but they gave me the impression of beings who were imprisoned, as if there was a mind which could be liberated if certain veils could be removed. The Mongol, under kindly conditions, has a very sweet disposition. The late Miss Macdowell, who had made a life-study of them, was always warm in praise of their disposition.

Hitherto, the treatment of this group has been very unsatisfactory; they should be tackled young, and treated on the general lines laid down here. In many cases Pineal and Thymus will probably be needed for a time. There is no form of disease which needs gland treatment more than the different varieties of mal-development, and these always need either Thymus or Pineal.

VI

I must leave out the research done on the thyroid, parathyroid, pituitary and adrenals for want of space. What I have worked out is already known, but there are certain aspects of these glands' action I want to emphasise: their relationship to the sex gland and their psychological actions. The accompanying diagram assists to impress the relationship on the memory ; it appears to me that the glands act on somewhat different levels of consciousness.   Even if the reader

DIAGRAM SHOWING ACTION OF GLANDS ON SEX GLAND.

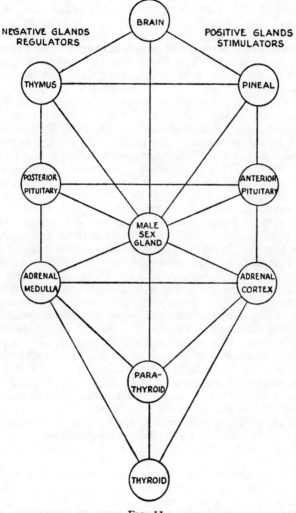

FIG. 11.

does not agree with my conclusions the diagram will help him to think and argue about the gland actions from his own experience. The stimulators of the male sex gland, which are positive, are placed on the right hand, the regulators, which are negative, on the left. The thyroid is a predominantly negative gland, but it stimulates the testes so it cannot be placed in either column ; the parathyroid is positive and controls or depresses the action of both sex glands, it must also have a neutral position. All the glands enter into mental and emotional actions, but it appears to me that they do so at different levels. The pineal is more closely allied to the higher mental levels than the other glands, but the thymus as a general controller acts on a higher level than the parathyroid. When the pineal is at a low level concentrated thought becomes difficult or impossible ; those who are suffering from mental overwork exhaust the pineal and benefit from its administration. The pineal is often found in lowered balance in people suffering from eye trouble or deafness, and it is increased in action during clairvoyance. It is also concerned in colour appreciation when sex glands are over-active and the trouble comes from the sex centre in the brain ; if a gland is needed for its correction Thymus is more often needed than Parathyroid. In any case where brain centres are involved with a psychological cause think first of Pineal and Thymus. If the primary cause be bacterial invasion think of Thyroid and Parathyroid. I have placed the Pituitary nearest to the Pineal level, for the Pineal and Pituitary are united with the colour-vision centre and Anterior Pituitary in addition to being connected with bodily strength is connected with a firm character and will-power. There are two classes of cases which give a considerable amount of trouble : boys who wet their beds and women who have a tendency to abort. They arise from the same cause : excess of posterior pituitary over anterior pituitary ; each portion of the gland enters into control of the uterus and bladder, and when a lack of balance occurs trouble ensues. The two classes of cases are caused by different reasons : boys wet their beds because they are deficient in anterior pituitary, and those who suffer from this trouble usually show the corresponding psychological symptoms. A lack of firm character, a tendency to take the easiest path, a kind of moral laziness. Women who abort readily do not show these mental characteristics, for they are not deficient in anterior pituitary, they have an excess of post pituitary ; the remedy for both cases is to balance the two portions of the gland and remove the toxæmia causing the condition. In the boys one has especially to remember that the symptoms are part of a condition usually carrying with it a general slackness of mental tone. Excess of anterior pituitary which has involved a change in growth does not mean a stronger character necessarily. I should say that the opposite is more often the case. I should feel a necessity for extra care in doing business with any person who had a congenital excess of any gland. We have, however, a censor within us, and no gland irregularity need necessarily mean moral deficiency. No hard and fast statement can be made that is not contradicted by facts ; all glands are concerned with emotions as I have shown and all are concerned with mind, but I should place pineal and pituitary as predominately mental glands, pineal with visualisation and imagination, and pituitary with will-power, and suprarenal and thyroid predominately with emotions. The two great controlling glands are thymus with mind and parathyroid with emotions and physical causes. For some cases of asthma thymus is deficient and of clinical value, and I should think of thymus in cases where there was not only over-sensitiveness to physical stimuli but to mental ones as well. I have placed the glands in the diagram in the position they occupy partly on physical reasoning but mainly on psychological. Bandler, in his book on endocrines, says he considers that pituitary is more often connected with psychical fears and cortex with physical. " If," he adds, " fears can be so divided." I have no doubt that they can be. Moral courage is a rarer quality than physical. I was once asked to report by blood examination on a boy who had furious attacks of temper ; when they occurred he ran away and hid. I found he had an excess of adrenalin and a very considerable deficiency of adrenal cortex. If he had had an equal excess of the gland of courage he would probably have been dangerous. People who are nervous of physical things have a deficiency of adrenal cortex. The pituitary and suprarenal are closely connected with control of the vascular system and may, therefore, be placed next to each other. I place the sex gland on a slightly higher level than the suprarenals, for though they are closely connected and devloped from neighbouring tissue, I consider that the sex gland is more closely connected with brain power than the suprarenal. When the sex gland is deficient creative mental power decreases. As a rule creative geniuses are over-sexed physically. There have been well-known cases to the contrary, but in these there may have been adequate internal secretion and sexual inadequacy may have been due to psychological frigidity rather than lack of hormones. The sex gland certainly can be said to be largely an emotional gland, but its mental effect must not be neglected. The thyroid is of all glands most essentially an emotional gland. At Burgess Hill and the villages north of the South Downs, enlarged thyroids were very common, but in seven years I do not remember a single case in a man. Enlargement of the thyroid began after puberty and had evidently a close connection with the ovaries ; the effects were not always those of secretion of the thyroid, but hyperthyroid periods were common and were always accompanied by a rise in emotion. The connection between thyroid and suprarenal is close, an excess of thyroid and adrenalin together are not unusual. The thyroid and suprarenal are therefore placed next each other. In this part of Sussex, in later life, ulcers on the legs were common among women. These healed well under the administration of Parathyroid. There was no need to give calcium, there was abundance of this in the water. I think it is probable that in a district where imbalance of the thyroid was very common in earlier life, the lack of parathyroid in the latter was a natural sequence; the two glands work together as I have shown, and an excess of one tends to produce a deficiency of the other. I never saw these ulcers on the legs in men. Women are naturally more emotional than men and the thyroid is essentially a negative or female gland. We may consider that the sex gland is physically and psychically the centre of our personality (not our individuality). If we have a testis we react emotionally and mentally in certain ways ; if we have an ovary we react quite differently. The diagram is intended to convey this. If the ovary is substituted for the testis in the diagram the posterior pituitary and the suprarenal medulla become stimulators and the anterior pituitary and cortex, regulators. The higher centre stimulator and control remain the same. Every gland has its share in varying importance all over the body, and no statement made about its importance in one direction can be made without someone finding an importance elsewhere. I have just seen a case of marked pineal deficiency with a very dry skin which suggested lowered thyroid, but this gland was normal in balance. The most marked symptom, however, was the inability to concentrate and great mental weariness. In physicist circles pictures are deprecated and mathematical formulæ preferred, but medicine has not yet reached this stage, and for the ordinary man a picture has some value : it catches the eye and stimulates thought and controversy, which aids again in knowledge. Some writers on the internal secretory glands appear to think we are entirely the creatures of our secretions. They object to the terms soul or spirit but they do not deny that effects of mind and emotion can alter gland secretion. There is always two-way traffic; impressions from outside forces can alter gland supply for good or evil. Total or almost entire absence of thyroid may produce a cretin with almost complete absence of mind, subthyroidism may produce or accompany a lack of *joie de vivre*, a lack of normal sex reaction, a shrinking from life. But cannot this same lack of thyroid and general subendocrine condition be produced by faulty bringing up, by allowing physical or psychical terrors to affect the mind and emotions in the early years of life. How much suffering of body is due to early environment, irrational religion, domination, or mere careless talk and threats !

There are three great aids to a good gland supply: mental freedom, rational discipline and a sound philosophy of life. At any rate in England we are tending that way ; the rising generation are on the whole in advance on their parents and more especially their grandparents. Extreme youth should remember, however, that their job is to help to form thought for the next generation, and that they will not make much impression on the thought of their day till they have had some experience of life. It is the repressions that so many of my generation have suffered from which has opened up life for their successors. To make fit commanders we must learn to obey not only those in authority, but first of all our own higher selves.

CHAPTER XII

THE BIOMORPHS

DURING the winter of 1929-30 I discovered a new form of matter. Hitherto I have been measuring the changes in atoms and the phenomena connected with them in health and disease. I had been pondering on the differences between minerals and life-forms. I had found that different animals, man, the dog, the cat, the horse, had certain secondary tunings when they were in health, for instance man has a balance-point at 37 ohms, the horse at 35, the dog at 35, worm 33.

The secondary tuning for man in good health for his whole body is 49,000 ohms, for horse, for the dog 38,000, worm 27,000.

I had found that a live organism will cause a repeat action on second rheostat when its highest intensity frequency is put upon two rheostats ; a dead one will not do this.

Discoveries sometimes come by what appears to be an accident, but this " accident " only occurs to minds ready to grasp the importance of the occurrence.

Since live forms showed differences in their electrical tunings I thought that something else might be found to distinguish live matter from the mineral.

Man was, according to my philosophy, body, soul and spirit ; many persons held the view that animals had something which persisted. These regions were perhaps outside my special work, but at the same time these were phenomena which I had discovered which showed that even in drug selection life-forces were the paramount consideration.

I had found that I must secure correct secondary tuning for man or beast when I prescribed for them. Further, I had learnt that mental symptoms were often given the best suggestion for obtaining the correct drugs for the patient. Then one evening after dinner, with Col. H. P. Lefroy, R.E., who had assisted me with advice and criticism, the idea was given me for research along new lines. Lefroy remarked that the things which happened in my circuit were enough to make one sick.

I agreed that from the view of pure physics this was the case, but that the various things which happened were due to life-forces. Lefroy agreed, and then said that he believed that there was a unit of life-force, the " bion," just as there was an electron and proton, and that if I sought for it I should find it.

Encouraged by Lefroy I went to work to seek this life-force. Hitherto I had always placed the delivery electrode to my subject along the centre line of the head except in the case of the recognition number. Work along the centre line of the head and down the spine had only resulted in tuning in to protons and electrons and obtaining different balance-points as described in the chapter on " Balance."

I started to go round the head instead of along its centre. I found four points on a level with the usual point of attach-ment above the nose, above the two eyes and on the same level at each side of the head just behind the eyes, where reactions were obtained of a different character.

At all four points I got a reaction when my rheostat was set at 11,111 ohms. To see if the areas varied I then tuned in with a second rheostat in series. I numbered the areas on the subject A, B, C, D.

A the area behind the left eye, B above the left eye, C above the right eye, D behind the right eye.

In each test I set the first rheostat at 11,111, then over A a reaction occurred with the second rheostat at 99,999. With B at 77,777, with C at 88,888, with D at 6,666.

I then obtained the following reactions on four rheostats in series. The dot over the figure indicates recurrence, a phenomena peculiar to these vibrations. Tuning with a fifth rheostat I got no further reactions :—A : $\dot{1}/\dot{9}/\dot{3}/\dot{2}$; B : $\dot{1}/\dot{7}/\dot{2}/\dot{9}$; C : $\dot{1}/8/4/\dot{6}$; D : $1/\dot{6}/8/4$.

These figures could only be obtained in this order ; an attempt to tune to $\dot{9}$ over A was useless until $11\dot{1}$ was placed on the first rheostat. $\dot{3}$ could not be tuned to except on the third rheostat with $\dot{1}$ on the first and $\dot{9}$ on the second. When the series $\dot{1}/\dot{9}/\dot{3}$ were put up $\dot{2}$ could be obtained on the 4th rheostat in series but in no other way.

The same phenomena occurred on the other areas.

The recurring figures and the covering layers were different from other reactions I had hitherto obtained.

This appeared to indicate considerable density of the layers. Each layer seemed to be so dense that the internal vibrations cannot escape till the outer layer has been tuned to.

Possibly dense is not the correct word or may not convey the correct meaning.

I conceive that the outer layers are so closely packed with

quickly moving bodies that the inner vibrations are masked by the outer layers.

I have called these bodies made up by a series of rings which surround each atom, compound and organ in the body, biomorphs. This name was given after consultation with Lefroy and a Greek dictionary. I could not call them bions as, though we conceived the bion was their basis, they were obviously compound bodies. " Bios," life, was an obvious start for a name, and they are forms of life, so that biomorph seems fairly suitable though it may not connote all that one would desire.

To test the plausibility of my conception I devised the following experiment :—

I took a gold nugget and wrapped it in lead, this again I wrapped in copper, and this I placed in a tin box. I put the tin box containing the other metals in the dynamiser. I tried to get a reflex for gold and failed, then for lead and copper, and in both cases failed. I then tuned in for tin on its atomic weight, 118·7, and obtained a good reflex, then on a second rheostat I put up 65·57 for copper, on a third 207·2 for lead and on a fourth 197·2 for gold.

In each case definite and clearly marked reflexes were obtained. When I varied the numbers no reflexes were obtained. I could only tune in to the elements in their due order and not otherwise. In this artificial system that I had made I had four frequencies present, a gold core and three layers outside it ; each layer was sufficiently dense to cover the others. In this way I had created a system which gave a similar tuning to the biomorphs. After having tuned in to the outer layer, tin, but not before, I could get in touch with the copper, and then having tuned in to the copper I could reach the lead, and eventually the gold. It is of interest to note that the reflex obtained when tuning in to tin and copper was harder than that obtained from tin alone. With the tuning for lead added the reflex was still harder, and when on four rheostats I had tuned into all the frequencies I got the hardest and best reflex of all. This means that when I had tuned in to the whole system the best result was. obtained. I had picked up the whole orchestra.

Having now given my general concept of the structure of the biomorph I will return to the consideration of the differences between biomorphs and elements.

In studying cases of disease I have found, as is described more fully in my chapter on Balance, that atoms in the diseased tissues give varied polarities, the balance of positive and negative is upset, the negative or positive frequency increasing whilst the other decreases. In the case of biomorphs, when there is a decrease or increase of biomorphic energy, the positive and negative energy are always equal. It would seem that for every positive bion there is always a negative bion, at any rate the intensity for both is always the same. They are probably like twin stars of equal mass.

Further, the biomorph gives rise to a frequency which is not accounted for by anything we know about the atom. I have shown elsewhere how all parts of the atom, as known to science, can be studied by human reflexes. When an element is placed in the circuit we obtain a reflex on its atomic number and atomic weight and we can always measure its positive, negative and neutral frequencies. All the above can be obtained when working with the electrode on the centre line of the head of the subject. If we move the electrode to the areas A, B, C, D we get additional frequencies, one for each area, and these are the same for all elements. They are not connected with any particular one, such as sulphur, cæsium or iron, but are common to every known element, and therefore, in all probability, to the unknown elements also. The biomorphs which cause these vibrations must be inter-atomic, for there is no other place in which they can be. At any rate they must occupy some part of the space hitherto known as ether. They are very dense bodies, and density is a character attributed to the ether. Does the ether, perhaps, consist of biomorphs ? If they are etheric bodies, and I think they must be, we have an indication that the ether is different in minerals from what it is in vegetables and animals and man. From minerals we get the following series of frequencies when the electrode is attached to the areas A, B, C, D. From A$\dot{2}$ from B$\dot{9}$, from C$\dot{6}$ and from D$\dot{4}$. These do not give the repeat phenomenon. From live plants we obtain, as before, the reflexes for the electrons in the elements, and from the areas A, B, C, D we get the biomorph frequency as follows : from A $\dot{3}/\dot{2}$, from B $\dot{2}/\dot{9}$, from C $\dot{4}/\dot{6}$, from D $\dot{8}/\dot{4}$. The mineral core is there but is covered by a new frequency. This series is peculiar to plant life and to that only. Micro-organisms give the vegetable series just as do the more complicated forms of plant life. What is the difference between organic compounds, which as we say live, and those which are merely chemicals ? Live matter can multiply, and in all cases it will be found to give the repeat reflex, and it contains double frequency biomorphs. If man could catch these double-frequency biomorphs and inoculate appropriate organic compounds he would create living forms.

From the lower numbers of the animal kingdom, such as beetles and flies, frogs and tortoises, biomorphs of threefold frequencies are obtained. The two frequencies of the vegetable from the A, B, C, D areas are reproduced, and each is surrounded by a fresh series peculiar to all forms of animal life thus: from A, 9/3/2, from B, 7/2/9, from C, 8/4/6, from D, 6/8/4.

Between vegetables and animals it is more difficult to find a separating line than between vegetables and minerals. The ingestion of food does not offer a sufficient distinction, nor is the power of locomotion a safe guide, but the presence of the third frequency in the biomorph may be considered a sure criterion.

Up to this point I have separated by life forms mineral, vegetable, animal, man.

There is such a vast difference between a mammal and an insect that I felt there must be some way of distinguishing between them. It seemed impossible that a companionable creature like the dog, who shares our pains and joys, sympathises in our sorrows, should have the same vital frequencies as the fly. Yet on the A, B, C, D areas on the head I was unable to get a further series. As regards three-circle biomorphs flies and dogs were alike.

I could get no further reaction from the A, B, C, D areas. The mammals are peculiar amongst other animals in their attachment to the mother before birth, and this though perhaps only partly consciously realised, let me try to tune in with the electrode held to the navel of the subject. When I tried with higher animals in the circuit I was able to pick up the following four series, and as they correspond obviously with the four series which I obtained on the A, B, C, D areas I will give them the same lettering, although it must be remembered in this case the electrode is held to the navel of the subject and not to the A, B, C, D areas. My series were as follows: A, 3/9/3/2; B, 3/7/2/9; C, 3/8/4/6; D, 3/6/8/4. I found that I could get these frequencies also along a line from the navel up towards the liver, for about an inch and a half. The line, I think, follows the remains of the Allantois vessels.

At each change in the biomorph structure we have a great jump in the life-form possessing these biomorphs. Minerals have but one, vegetable two, lower animals three and higher animals, such as mammals, four frequencies. With a human being in the circuit and the electrode on the navel of the subject, I obtained a fifth frequency, so that from a human being we get the following four series of frequencies: A, 3/1/9/3/2; B, 3/1/7/2/9; C, 3/1/8/4/6; D, 3/1/6/8/4. These series of five frequencies indicate the presence of a five-fold biomorph in human beings.

To make things clear I will again list the biomorphs in each class of beings :—

Minerals : one-ring biomorphs.
Vegetables : two-ring biomorphs.
Insects and reptiles : three-ringed biomorphs.
Mammals and birds : three-ring and four-ring bio-
morphs.
Man : four-ring and five-ring biomorphs.

I have given this list as it relates how the research proceeded, and it may prove of importance in future work.

The question, however, arises : Do men and animals actually have two sets of these life-forms or is this merely apparent owing to the fact that I have tapped them on a different area of the indicator's body ?

Working on A, B, C, D areas gives a different result to working on the navel.

Working at the latter point each atom in man appears to be surrounded by these five layers—with animals it is four layers, for if I tune to the atomic number of any element or compound with a sixth rheostat I get a reflex. Hence it would appear that each atom, compound or organ, has a series of layers of biomorphic material round it and this can be tuned to the navel on the subject.

When we come to study the aura it will be seen that similar frequencies surround the whole body.

It seems to me that these phenomena suggest that Darwin's general idea of evolution is true : one form of life has evolved from the simpler form, else why do we perpetuate the simpler life forms ?

Over the pregnant uterus in the early months I have picked up the reptile form of biomorph, and later the mammalian, before the human form arrives.

You can, if you please, think that each form arrived by a special act of creatoin. In a sense this must of necessity be so, for if the universe is the thought of God, the Great Architect, the added form of life arrived by His thought when the time was ripe for its arrival. It was doubtless in His thought when from the beginning of time predetermined for our planet, and the question whether things grew by themselves from a primordial stimulus, or by an ever-present thought and care, is a matter of temperament of the thinker.

In the eternal I conceive there can be no beginning or end, but constant being, so with His creation or thought.

Creative power goes on all the time. The question of growth versus creation seems really futile. Evolution or change is one of our certainties ; we and our bodies change from moment to moment, the flora of our intestines is constantly changing, changes in biomorphs occur during disease. I shall presently describe changes in the aura. but I first started observations on the body and I will take these first.

In cancer and sarcoma the B group of biomorphs are affected, and not in any other condition. In inflammatory diseases the C group, and either A or D, is affected. Always two groups are affected and the other two remain apparently normal. In a case of merftal weariness I found A and D down ; there was no trace of bacterial disease.

Working on the four biomorphs, the first change noticed is that the i series disappears, and we tap in place of this the animal tuning. In cancer in place of the human series we get a series beginning with the animal and vegetable rings but with another added frequency inside the ordinary mineral frequency. In place of the healthy form $\dot{\text{i}}/\dot{7}/\dot{2}/\dot{9}$ I find $\dot{7}/\dot{2}/\dot{9}/\dot{3}$.

In several cases I have found a further change to $\dot{2}/\dot{9}/\dot{6}/\dot{9}$, i.e. beginning with the vegetable type of tuning. In a hand affected by cold, which was blue and without feeling, I got the vegetable rings only. Similar changes take place in inflammatory diseases. A frozen hand is partially dead ; some of its life has left it for the time being and, unless circulation is restored, the biomorph change will go further still.

The changes in the five biomorphs will be described in the next chapter, under the auric changes. It will be seen that sleep somewhat resembles diseases.

Changes in the A and D biomorphs I have not worked out thoroughly, but when A changes I have found the thyroid affected, with D sex changes.

These frequencies are undoubtedly due to life, they are absent in dead matter except for the mineral forms. The same change occurs in loss of consciousness whether due to natural sleep, trance or an anæsthetic.

II
THE AURA

The frequencies I have described in the human and animal bodies I found were duplicated in the atmosphere or aura surrounding the body.

Some years ago Dr. Kilner, who was radiologist at St. Thomas's Hospital, wrote a book called " The Human Atmosphere " in which he described the aura as made visible by the use of a solution of dicyanin to sensitise the eyes.

Kilner's work was not entirely original, for Baron von Reichenbach had many years before discovered persons who could see rings of light round the points of a magnet, and discovered that different metals gave off different coloured lights which could be seen by these sensitives.

Kilner described a layer of half an inch in width which he called the etheric double, a layer of about 4 inches round the head bluish and granular in texture, which he called the inner aura, and an outer aura of nearly the same width of greyish blue finer in texture. On very favourable occasions he saw something beyond this.

The visible aura varies in shape in man and woman and in disease.

Kilner was most careful in his observations and statements and was conservative in stating that the aura visible with eyes sensitised by dicyanin to be an emanation from the nervous system.

Kilner further used coloured glasses to examine the aura and described dark patches over diseased areas.

For details of the visible aura Kilner's book should be read.

I am told that the aura has measured in Angstrom units, but it by no means follows that what I have measured corresponds to this or to Kilner's observations ; the body may give off a number of different emanations.

As regards biomorphic frequencies the aura is a replica of what I have already described ; the human aura consists of five layers and a narrow circlet which lies between the first two rings.

The colours were first worked out by finding out what coloured films increased the intensity of the vibrations. It was found on experiment that the intensity of a blue object was increased by blue, red by red, yellow by yellow ; also that the closer the tint of the coloured film to the object the greater the intensity.

Later this was checked by working out the highest intensity

frequency of a number of films and finding out which film corresponded to the various layers.

The rings from within outwards are as follows :—

Origin	Frequency	Colour	Width	Colour frequency
Mineral ..	A2 B9 C6 D4	Blue ..	½ inch	
Comes in } with life } ..	11,111	.. Pale yellow	⅛ inch	
Vegetable ..	A3 B2 C4 D8	Red ..	4 inches	
Reptile ..	A9 B7 C8 D6	Orange ..	4 inches	
Mammal ..	11,111	.. Yellow ..	4 inches	
Human ..	33,333	.. Various ..	9 to 10 or more feet	

When I tested the 3 frequency in the fifth ring in man I found variety. Each individual had in health a personal colour, and in disease a colour corresponding to the condition.

When I had worked out this series of coloured rings I consulted Mr. H. Buckingham as to what colours he saw. I found that his vision corresponded to what I had worked out by measurement.

I had previously asked two clairvoyants, who have the gift of seeing the aura naturally without the aid of dicyanin solution (which Kilner used) to examine a case of sarcoma and report on his condition. One was Mr. H. Buckingham and the other Mr. Michael Thomas. They saw the patient within a few days of each other. Their reports were practically identical. Both reported the same affected areas and agreed on the number of layers affected. Both spotted a faint cloud on the chest where an injection of arsenic had been given a year before. Both said this showed as a faint grey cloud affecting only one layer of the aura.

Mr. Thomas described a slowing of the vital currents over the affected areas. Their reports as to density of colour and layers affected tallied. In cancer they agreed that the worst affected parts were black, less infected dark brown, light brown ; least of all, grey.

I have had frequent opportunities of checking up Mr. Buckingham's vision as to the situation and intensity of lesions, and have always found he was right. In some cases he spotted things I was ignorant of, for instance he spotted an alteration in auric colour over an old fracture in my subject, which neither Mr. Buckingham nor myself knew existed.

In the case examined both clairvoyants found the darkest spot on the same position on the lung, which was painful.

My measurements showing the colour of the auric rings

were therefore confirmed by sight by one whom I have always found correct.

A considerable number of people can see the aura under suitable conditions, to a limited extent, without the use of dicyanin solution to sensitise the eyes. I should say that at least ten per cent. can see the rays coming off the fingers if they are opposed to each other against a dark background with just sufficient light to see the outline of the hands. Under these conditions grey strands can be seen passing from one hand to the other, across some six inches in a healthy person. After oscilloclast treatment the distance the rays pass from one hand to the other is increased to about ten inches. Under good conditions three rays can be seen from the three inner fingers passing to different opposing fingers ; I can see this myself. Practice increases one's vision. On one occasion, sitting in the dark when I was tired, I saw and described the colours in Buckingham's outer aura. He knew what they were, so this can be ascribed to thought trans-ference, but the appearance at the time was clear enough. This power of seeing what is not usually seen by others is much more common that is supposed. I have met a number of people who have what is called clairvoyance. They have most of them had a bad time during their childhood, as they were accused of wilful lying. Parents should encourage special gifts instead of checking them. Sometimes their power is merely confined to seeing the aura, sometimes it is extended to seeing what are popularly called ghosts. A friend of ours in India saw ghosts or thought-forms or whatever they may be, so solid in appearance that she mistook them for living flesh and blood ; this was sometimes embarrassing as she had no wish to appear peculiar. Most clairvoyants can put this power on and off at will by concentration, and those in the flesh then become dim while concentration on a different plane is used.

An interesting question arises as to whether such forms are really part of the individuality of persons, in or out of the flesh, or merely thought-forms. A friend of mine was nearly run over by a taxi dodging such a form, which appeared solid and also dodged him. The taxi-driver's language was loosened at the apparent imbecile trying to avoid a non-existent person. The spectre also did a double shuffle, which shows a mind behind the apparent solidity. My friend had several unex-pected visions of the sort without ever taking a single tot, although he can turn his special gift on and off almost at will.

It is really extraordinarily stupid to deny the appearance of ghosts. The evidence that some people have special powers of vision is ample. Because it appears more frequently among Easterners or among primitive people some Westerners deny the phenomena altogether, or they call it " occultism " and sturdily disapprove of the investigation of perfectly natural phenomena.

There are a number of books with accounts of such phenomena.

If however we are to know all about man's functions we must not discard any evidence. As far as possible we must examine this and measure it.

Death means loss of the auric frequencies, sleep a change, and disease—the prelude to death in many cases—also a change, but an irregular change. In very sick people the outer layer may be reduced to about two feet. In cancer I find the third layer of B biomorphs is reduced from four inches to as little as half an inch ; its intensity, which should be 111,111 ohms, may be as little as 11 ohms. Similar changes take place in inflammatory conditions, but seldom to the same extent. The aura changes then in disease in two ways : in alteration of the width of the bands, and in the intensity of the frequencies. In some cases one band is greatly increased and overlaps the others. In one case, where the liver was badly infected, the mineral layer, corresponding to Kilner's etheric double, was increased from half an inch to six inches in front of the liver, behind the body this layer was only an inch wide. I found a much slighter increase in a case where shock played an important part. Both cleared up during treatment.

As a test of general condition I measure the outer aura. It should be picked up ten feet away from a plate at the distal end on my circuit. With appropriate colours and drugs in the circuit this can be felt twenty feet away, with the patient the other side of a closed door. Auric frequencies pass through wood as if it was not there.

These measurements are all made by upending the plate on which the patient usually sits and getting the patient to retreat until the reflex on my subject, measured on 3, disappears.

Seeing ghosts of the living, or the so-called dead, is only an extension of auric vision, which is existent in at least one in ten persons to a limited extent.

When I was younger I could hear a bat squeak ; before I left India I had lost this power. My old chief, Dr. Andrew of Bart.'s, could hear heart murmurs better than his house physician, when he was deaf to the ordinary tones of conversation. Our powers vary with training.

The aura during sleep, and under an anæsthetic, and also during trance, loses its three outer layers. I have only been able to examine one case during sleep ; there are obvious difficulties, but a patient under ionisation went to sleep in my room and we were able to examine him. My subject pointed the distal electrode at him from my cage, some six feet away. Had the patient been awake we should only have picked up the outer aura-frequency, 3. We only obtained frequencies belonging to the vegetable type. I have, however, examined several bloods, taken from patients under an anæsthetic ; the same phenomena occurred. On one occasion I examined a friend who can go into a voluntary trance. First of all the outer layer of aura disappeared from his body, and then from his aura, the electrode being pointed to the side of his body. The second layer went next from his body, and then from his aura, and later the third disappeared. They reappeared as he gradually became conscious, in the reverse order, first in the aura, then on his body.

Where do they go to ? I have no experimental evidence to give you so far. It is however clear that you cannot lose consciousness with the full tide of life in you.

People not infrequently tell you they have had the experience of coming across places they knew quite well, though they have never consciously been there before. They sometimes imagine this is due to memories from a former life. If some portion of our consciousness is detached during sleep, projection to a distance is not impossible, and this may account for the phenomena. Read Dunn's book " An Experiment in Time." His dream experiences can be explained by such a projection. In such a fourth dimensional condition visions of the future may well be possible. I have met a number of persons who have experienced such projections during sleep. The brother of an old medical friend of mine, during such a projection, saw his body lying apparently dead, with red spots on the face. A year or more later he died of septicæmia, and had a septicæmic rash.

I use auric frequencies for the final test as to whether colours, drugs, vaccines or glands are needed for treatment. A drug or vaccine may be found suitable to remedy certain changes in balance, but when tried on the aura it may be quite unsuitable. I am able in this way to reduce the number of vaccines and drugs indicated for treatment. Diet is also selected by its influence on these life forces.

The aura has been outlined by its effect on neon lamps.

Lately Dr. Temple Sylvester has made me an instrument for measuring the intensity of forces in the aura. It consists of a shield and a neon lamp. The person under examination stands on a plate charged with high frequency. This does not apparently increase the extent of the visible aura, but merely agitates it. Under these conditions, when the screen is between three or four feet from a healthy person, the lamp lights up. This is not only an ocular demonstration of the presence of the auric field, but is of practical use, as the effect of a suitable dose will increase the distance at which the lamp lights. The testing lamp may be attached to earth or to the observer's hands, by a wire to each. The distance reading when the wires go to earth is somewhat less than when the observer holds the wires. The distance is affected if the observer at the wires be changed. A strong healthy person on the wires will give a greater distance reading for each patient than weak one. The best method to ensure steady readings is to earth the lamp.

The following were the results of a series of doses given when we first tested the apparatus, an observer taking the place of an earth.

Distance before dose		Dose given	Distance afterwards
(1)	38 in.	100c orchitic	45 in.
(2)	50 in.	Red colour	56 in.
(3)	43 in.	100c orchitic	59 in.
(4)	38 in.	Aluminium 30	42 in.
(5)	32 in.	Strep. vaccine	41 in.
(6)	35 in.	Coli vaccine	38 in.

When an endocrine potency can be given a big change occurs. I took a tablet of thyroid and potassium permanganate in my mouth ; as it began to melt the lamp went out, I had to step forward to light it up again. The same effect can be got by holding a high potency which is not needed.

The electrode from the high-frequency apparatus can be brought quite close to the lamp screen or aerial without causing the lamp to light. It would be quite feasible with a neon lamp on a suitable carrier to map out the aura and observe places where it is deficient.

I have not been able at present to work out what it is acts on the neon lamp—whether the lighting-up is due to electronic discharges or biomorphs or a combination of both.

The distance at which the lamp acts is in the outer aura ; a situation where, owing to masking by the 333 layer, I have failed to pick up purely electronic elements. We are, however, not sufficiently advanced at present to lay down the law on this subject. The 333 layer in whose area the lamp lights belongs to a portion of our personality which is removed during sleep. It is hard to believe that this apart from the body could light up a lamp ; it is easier to believe that the lighting is due to the entire series of vibrations, one within the other, representing the entire electro-magnetic field.

Experiments with the aura and its layers may show us the physiological connection of those parts of our system which are as much a necessary part of our being as our brain and liver.

We can *never* know anything about this *living* part of our personality unless we keep absolutely open minds on the subject. The study of the aura is the bridge between living and dead matter, between what we choose to call material and a different kind of material which seems immaterial. This material we can measure as biomorphs. We can also measure the simulacrum of protons and electrons. Of every kind of physical phenomena which I can measure from the earth matter plane, I can get a corresponding measure from the thought plane. Yet measured thought forms have no aura and do not repeat ; we can make a picture but cannot bestow life.

There are certain life-centres connected with the aura : (1) The heart and lung centre, on a spot halfway between the left nipple and midline of the body. When this is affected something deep in the personality is affected. This may be measured on the surface of the patient, or in the aura. The 11,111 layer is often affected. (2) The splanchnic plexus centre about an inch above the navel, connected with all abdominal organs, except sex organs, and also with the emotional states. 888 or 11,111 is affected. (3) Sex centre, the lower part of the lumbar spine, or just above the pubes. It includes the bladder and the lower portion of the rectum and the legs. Where there is a marked sex under or over action, all these parts may suffer. An unfortunate love affair may affect this area and the heart, the aura being depressed in each case. The sex area and the heart are closely connected. The connections need working out. (4) There is also a centre over the episternal notch, which is of the greatest importance in cancer cases. This centre should always be treated in cancer by colour. The importance of this centre is not confined to cancer. The effect of colour on this spot can be demonstrated by use of the neon lamp. There is no anatomical structure which is known to account for this. I have demonstrated the effect of colour on this spot by cutting off the surrounding parts with a lead screen. The greatest effect of the colour is definitely shown over this spot by the way the lamp lights up when the colour is shone on the spot. If the spot is covered and the thyroid exposed to the colour the lamp will go out, when the patient remains at the greatest distance at which he will light the lamp, whilst the colour is over the episternal notch. I have inquired of clairvoyants, but this centre was unknown to them. It is not mentioned in books on occultism as far as I know.

In India the yogis teach that there is a special flow of Prana in the region of the thyroid and from the top of the head, which appears to be connected with the pineal gland.

I have lately made the discovery that the repeat phenomena, indicating life, are very closely connected with the layers of the aura. A vegetable will repeat on two rheostats, a live insect on three, a mammal on four, and a man on five ; that is, any frequency can be repeated on two, three, four or five rheostats, and an abdominal reflex will follow so long as the substance is a live vegetable, insect, mammal or human.

This repeat action is of great value in testing, for we can decide whether the substance we are testing is merely mineral matter or vegetable or due to a human cell change.

The aura of the four stages in evolution preceding man work out as follows :—

Class	Width	Frequency	Colour
Mineral	2 in.	A2̇ B9̇ C6̇ D4	Blue
Vegetable (small plant)	½ in.	A2̇ B9̇ C6̇ D4	Blue
	⅛ in.	2222̇	Yellow
	2 in.	A3̇ B2̇ C4̇ D8̇	Red
Reptile and Insect—			
Worm	2 in.	A2̇ B9̇ C6̇ D4	Blue
	⅛ in.	1111̇	Yellow
	1 in.	A3 B2 C4 D8	Red
	1 in.	A9 B7 C8 D6	Orange
Mammal: Bull terrier	½ in.	A2 B9 C6 D4	Blue
	⅛ in.	5555̇	Yellow
	1½ in.	A3 B2 C4 D8	Red
	1 in.	A9 B7 C8 D6	Orange
	4½ ft.	3333	Yellow

It will be seen that the mammal type approximates to the human, the outer ring has the colour of the fourth ring of the human, but has a similar frequency to the outer human and is rather less than half its width.

It is possible that constant contact of the domesticated

dog with human beings has altered the aura ; this I have had no opportunity to investigate. A wild dog in my cage might be difficult to measure even if I could get him there.

I have done some research on changes in the aura due to emotions, but it needs repeating. The various frequencies change during emotions, some being increased and others being diminished during states of emotion and in varying ways according to the emotion exhibited.

The outer ring of the human aura which gives the 3 vibrations .shows a series of coloured rings when seen by clairvoyants ; when measured these are a series of rings from red to violet which I have picked up on colour frequencies each about $\frac{1}{4}$ inch across ; these all appear to measure about the same intensity on my apparatus, and I do not know why only certain colours are seen by clairvoyants. By measurement the whole spectrum is present. Probably some layers are brighter than others, but this does not show on my apparatus. These are situated just outside the yellow layer, i.e. about 13 to $16\frac{1}{2}$ inches outside the head ; these are certainly connected with health.

III

WHAT IS THE AURA ?

I am often asked if the aura is the etheric body or the astral or both. One answer can be given easily : the frequencies in the bands of colour and the colours do not constitute a body, they are merely the life forces in the body and around it. If you consider the chemical body alone apart from the life forces due to its being human, the inner ring and its corresponding frequencies inside the body may be considered the etheric of the minerals, for the auric frequencies penetrate the atoms and surround each nucleus. Let us for the sake of argument allow there are other bodies in addition to the chemical body which we all see and feel. Each ring of auric colour and frequencies inside the body would form a kind of ether for a corresponding body. I have not the space nor the evidence I require to argue in detail about this subject. The " Chain of Life " would not however be complete unless I mentioned it. The only evidence my own work gives is that there is something.in our life forces which separates from the physical body during sleep or under an anæsthetic, that is when we lose consciousness. It would, however, be just as foolish to ignore evidence of others' experience in this matter,

as it would be to ignore others' work in medicine. There
is a considerable amount of literature bearing on the subject
of conscious projection during sleep. One book is " The Astral
Body," by Carrington and Muldoon. I have met several
persons who have had this experience and one who drew a
plan of my room before he entered it in the flesh. He showed
this to a mutual friend and also gave details of other parts of
the house which were unknown to this friend. Some of the
persons who have consciously projected during sleep have
been seen by others while doing so. Such an appearance
might be due to a thought form, but a thought form could not
obtain knowledge of things at a distance, which has certainly
been done during sleep or trance. The term etheric is variously
used. Some use it to mean something akin to Kilner's
etheric double, others use it as a general term for matter which
is not physical. Astral also seems to be rather vaguely used.
Sometimes for the whole body which is separable from the
physical during sleep, sometimes for a body corresponding
to the emotions. Writers who deal with this subject usually
under the heading " Occultism," divide man's being into
seven bodies, they usually either copy Eastern terms or trans-
late them into terms which have as little meaning for the
ordinary man as the original. Certain Western psychologists
have divided the whole man into the following states of
consciousness :—

7. Abstract spiritual.
6. Concrete spiritual.
5. Abstract mind.
4. Concrete mind.
3. Higher instincts.
2. Lower instincts.
1. Physical.

From the occult point of view they consider there are seven
bodies corresponding to seven states of consciousness, but from
the psychological point of view we can get some interesting
correlation between states of consciousness and the auric rings.

If we consider the foregoing classification of consciousness
we find that each added ring of the aura corresponds to a step
up in consciousness. The headings in col. 2 of the following
table are due to a lecture on psychology given by Dr. T. Penry
Evans, though I have modified his table to suit the comparison
between man and animals. Under " Concrete Mind " he gave
" Search for Truth." This does not apply to animals ;
" Reasoning " does.

1 State of consciousness	2 Sign of state	3 Class	4 Rings in aura	5 Example
Abstract mind	Wisdom	Man	5	
Concrete mind	Reasoning	Mammal	4	Dogs, horses, parrots, rooks
Higher emotions	Herd instinct	Insects	3	A n t s, B e e s, wasps
Lower instincts	S e x a n d self-preservation	Vegetables	2	The higher grades of plants
Physical	Polarity. Chemical affinity	Minerals	1	

In the vegetable world self-preservation may be said to begin with micro-organisms with their power of changing their nature according to the soil they find themselves in and their enormous power of multiplication. Self-preservation is shown in more complicated forms of plant life by their efforts to reach soil or light, or avoid light as lichens do. Then there are the complicated mechanisms for obtaining and digesting nitrogen as shown by the sundews and Venus' fly-trap. Mechanisms for propagation by sexual methods are various, polarity has now definitely become sex. In the insects herd instinct appears, clearly shown in the case of ants, bees and wasps. I have no great acquaintance with reptiles, but with ants I have some experience. During the hot weather in Scinde I was stationed on the railway on plague duty ; I had part of the evening to wander in the thorn scrub, the most interesting inhabitants being the ants. I found a long trail of worker ants carrying grain; some workers carried bits of thorn and other rubbish. I followed up to the entrance of the nest. Rubbish and thorn-carriers came out quicker than they went in, generally attached to their burden. On opening up the entrance I found two powerful ants of ferocious aspect acted as door warders and " chuckers-out." Anything dead was heaved out promptly. Probably any good field naturalist would supply plenty of other examples. Then among moths and flies there are curious foreseeing actions for the good of the future young. I gave an example in Chapter I : in India there is a fly which paralyses green caterpillars, lays its eggs in them and walls them up in mud, frequently in keyholes. Chemico-wireless may help to explain many of these actions, but they illustrate instincts which benefit others of the species, one step-up on plants. In animals, particularly dogs and monkeys, it is not necessary for me to argue about the presence of concrete mind. Anyone who has kept dogs or studies them knows all about it. Read Richardson's " Forty Years with Dogs " if you have not done so already. Any big game hunter will tell you stories which show wild animals use their heads to avoid or catch you. Animals have brains and use them. Dogs certainly have a sense of humour. Birds also have four ringed auras and in them concrete mind is emergent. I know a parrot who says " good night " repeatedly till he is covered up at night, " good-bye " when you get up to go, or " good-bye " when he wants his mistress to go and get supplies, or scatters his grain if he wants a fresh supply.

Once in my childhood I saw a rook trial and execution. The rooks formed a large ring, the criminal faced a large dominant rook who was evidently in charge and did most of the cawing, the criminal replied feebly ; occasionally individual rooks made a remark. After a considerable period the judge gave a loud caw and the whole lot flew up and pecked the prisoner to death. Poultry breeders will tell you something about the difference in hens as mothers. One hen will bring up her entire setting as well-grown chicks, taught to scratch to take dust-baths and do all that chickens should do. Another hen will lose half or more of her brood by clumsiness, the chickens that survive are poor things in weight, devoid of chicken arts and crafts.

Each stage in evolution has its own particular stage in consciousness, but there are varying states in each class. Man in the lowest state known to us has faculties in consciousness beyond the animal, but the higher stage is only gradually emergent. I have shown that the number of rings in the aura correspond with stages of consciousness but they are neither mind nor body, only the vital energy in the body ; they do not give form or function, but they correspond to stages in evolution in body and states of consciousness.

I may be expressing an opinion on a subject of which I have very little knowledge, but it seems to me that though the term etheric body is suitable to the auric frequencies of the first ring which do form an ether or interpenetrating substance for the mineral body, the term astral is extremely vague and that it would be better to speak of other bodies in terms of the psychological classification given above. The time may come when we can prove their existence scientifically by measurement, just as the auric frequencies and colours have been measured. Whoever carries out this work will have to build on the scaffolding I have erected. The bodies corresponding to the rings are probably made up of atoms and molecules just as our physical body is. It is possible to cause reactions for atoms and molecules by mental action, and in fact everything must exist in mind as well as in physics. If atoms do not exist on the mental plane you could not conceive of them. As I show later, thoughts can be picked up on the circuit and facts unknown to the observers worked out from them. Apparitions of the dead must be mere thought forms, and in my experiments thoughts of individuals carry no aura. But where a projected consciousness is seen, some kind of a body must be present to give form. The mental plane gives form and in accordance with occult teaching each plane is ensouled by the one above it in consciousness. The emotional body should therefore have something in the way of matter to give it form. To anyone who has been able to appreciate that unseen matter can be measured, this is no difficulty. Mentally, there may be atoms of emotion or there may be other matter, neither atomic nor biomorphic nor in the nature of light. The emotions affect all these in the body and in the aura. We have the electron, the proton and the bion. There may be a unit of emotion and also of spirit. The latter is out of our reach in our present wrappings, but if there is a unit of emotion it may be possible to find it hereafter. I do not include in the aura the physical magnetic field. I contend, however, that all manifestations of life are physics, but physics on varying planes, and that it is our business to demonstrate this. We must realise that all matter, including the rocks, was mind matter before it was earth matter, that the mind forces of the Creator are behind all phenomena. Similarly in our own researches we can find nothing that is not represented in our own mind. A fact must be conceived mentally before it is looked for ; in the case of the biomorphs discovery followed Col. Lefroy's conception of the bion.

Knowledge in the conscious mind may come out of the subconscious, but usually only after much painstaking experiment. In the words of the old proverb, " God helps those who help themselves."

Before leaving the subject of the aura there are two questions which may be asked : Were there ever single ringed forms of life ? Will man or another race have six or seven rings in the course of evolution ? I think we may certainly conclude that the first step in evolution was that organic compounds became alive. A chunk of chemicals acquired a life circlet forming a single form of plant life. I remember one glorious evening when one of my sons and other disputants out-Darwined Darwin and reconstructed this globe and its contents. P. J. absolutely refused to allow plants to evolve into animals, and the argument swung round that point till I insisted on catching the last 'bus home. Quite possibly the original stock which grew into man, animals and plants, separated in the one-ringed class. In man we find the three-ringed type of life during the first month of life in the uterus. Nature has no breaks ; I have never found a single-ringed creature, but it must have existed once if it does not do so now. The Eastern method of obtaining knowledge is to go into a trance state or to raise consciousness to a higher level by meditation ; this requires a strict course of discipline and training ; those who have practised this method assure us that man, animals and plants evolved by separate stocks, and that we are now in the fifth race of men. We have five rings in our aura which, as we have seen, corresponds to a certain degree of progress in states of consciousness. The next race should have six rings and develop a higher state of spiritual consciousness. At present the world is divided into people who imagine that everything is true and accepted which comes into knowledge either by the Western or Eastern method ; extreme advocates of either method pour foul scorn on the other. The time will come when knowledge gained from the physical end will meet that gained from the spiritual side ; one will correct the other. In the meantime we have to use anything presented to us with modesty and scepticism. Not thinking we know better than experts, but remembering that any method, however marvellous, leaves room for mistakes when used by fallible men and women. When the seven-ringed aura race possesses the earth it should make a greater success of things than we are doing. Before there can be heaven above there must be heaven below.

IV

MENTAL COLOURS

Overlying the frequencies and colours I have described are colours seen by certain seers which are ascribed to the mind. Mr. Buckingham has described to me a yellow colour lying within four inches of the body over the red which he says varies with the condition of the patient's mind. I have not yet been able to verify this variation, but the colour measures 36,910 ohms and corresponds to a certain film I possess. Mr. Neal, another capable seer whose powers are well known, describes a series of colours in this position ; he apparently does not see the rings I have described. In viewing the aura it appears you have to concentrate on various layers. If you usually look for the mental plane colours you get those and no others. The colours described by Mr. Neal I have picked up in my subject's aura and in my own, but so far I cannot substantiate by measurement or observation that they are due to mind or character. To do this will take some years of steady research. To prove they are due to mind one must find that they vary in mental disease constantly.

Since writing the above I have found colours in the aura going out to 10 feet. The layers are from within outwards, arranged as follows :—

Blue ..	..	..	..	½ inch
Yellow	..	..	..	¼ inch
Red ..	..	..	..	4 inches
Orange	..	..	..	4 inches
Yellow	..	..	..	4 inches
Red	..	..	..	
Orange	..	..	..	
Yellow	..	..	..	covering
Green	..	..	..	3½ inches
Blue	..	..	..	
Violet	..	..	..	
Ultra-violet		..	..	17 inches to 83 inches
Blue	..		..	83 inches to 94 inches
		Yellow streamers from body to 10 feet		

The spectrum covering the space from 13 to 17 inches is present in all cases examined. Clairvoyants see a portion of these colours only. The brilliance they see of certain colours must be due to some mental effect, for the spectrum measures the same intensity for all colours in every healthy person.

The colours in this part of the aura are said to vary with character. I have no knowledge in regard to this.

My own visible spectrum extends from red to green, Mr. Buckingham's from violet to yellow.

Until an immense amount of work has been done on a number of cases I am sceptical in regard to statements about character reading by auras by any set rules, though there may be some connection.

In conclusion, I must beg my readers to suspend judgment as to the exact nature of the aura. Some consider that it must be composed of astral matter, since it is connected with a portion of the personality which disappears during trance or sleep. Others consider that it is etheric in nature, i.e., a purely physical phenomena. Some state that this must be so, since it has been measured by physical means. We have, however, to allow for the fact that Abrams introduced a new mode of measurement, using life to study life. Whatever the nature of the outer aura may be, our subject or detector is also human, and has in his body and aura similar frequencies to those of the person we are studying, Proof, therefore, one way or the other is difficult. We can only make deductions which are sure to be coloured by our mental attitude. The safest plan is to record observations and go on making them till further evidence is obtained and the subject better understood. The one thing the researcher must not do is to let the thought " impossible " enter his mind.

PART III

CHAPTER XIII

RECOGNITION OF DISEASED CONDITIONS

I HAVE described in Chapter II how Abrams recognised diseases on certain numbers which turned out to be atomic numbers. This proved to be unsatisfactory, for though he was, I believe, right in saying that a change occurred in the 55-ohm reaction in syphilis, probably in all cases, and at 50 ohm in cancer, perhaps in all cases, certainly changes occur in 50 in staphylococcal infections as well. Every physician knows the value of tin, the 50th element in certain staphylococcal infections of the skin. This could be of no value unless the balance of the tin molecules were upset, in which case 50 would and does give an altered reaction. Most of Abrams' followers have by now discovered there is an inflammatory 50 as well as that indicating the presence of cancer. In any case there have been plenty of errors made and it is quite unsafe to recognise the condition by changes in one atom. In serious conditions like cancer and advanced syphilis changes occur in almost every atom in the body to a greater or less extent.

I am told that Abrams was wonderfully good at diagnosis, but one must allow for two things : one he was a very able physician in other ways than by his special method, which he only elaborated in the latter part of his life, and also for the symbols he used acting as a psychological index. A good deal of correct diagnosis and choice of remedy in experienced physicians is done by a kind of subconscious intuition.

I can quite believe that a man may believe that a 50 reaction is always indicative of cancer and yet make very few actual mistakes because he does not get this reaction with non-malignant cases ; some inhibition blocks it out.

This sort of flair can only be obtained by long experience and the beginner needs more reliable data. If Abrams made but few mistakes it was in spite of his method, not because of it. This detail of his method by itself is apt to lead to error.

Having come to the conclusion that Abrams' method of

diagnosis was unsatisfactory in my own case, I sought for a more satisfactory method. My first attempt to recognise organisms was by studying the conditions by which they were recognised in the laboratory. I started with the non-lactose group of organisms as I was working with Dr. Edward Bach. I found that if an organism would affect lactose it would cause a reaction on the molecular weight of lactose ; if it would not do so it gave no reaction on this number. The same thing happened with other media. I further used colour tests to separate out organisms. All this took some time and I sought for a better method.

My first hint of what to do was given me by an article by Dr. O. M. Hayward of U.S.A. on taking a personal rate for a patient. Hayward was trying to find the wave from the oscilloclast (Abrams' treatment apparatus) which would be the best for the patient as a whole. He was in homœopathic terms seeking the similimum. The frequency which best expressed the needs of the whole individual. I applied this to endocrines and diseased organisms. The substance to be tested was placed in the testing circuit and was tuned in till the reflex on the subject's abdomen became quite hard.

The coils of the circuit were then opened till the reflex died away with no figures on the rheostats, the figure previously arrived at was then hoisted and if the reflex retuned good and hard I concluded we had a satisfactory recognition number. We have now got about 950 different recognition numbers without repetition. Only in one or two instances have we had to alter our original findings for recognition numbers.

Of course there are cross correspondences between drugs and organisms. A tubercle bacillus of the Koch variety gives off a wave corresponding to nux vomica and pulsatilla, and calc. carb. among other connections. If this were not so these drugs could have no effect on the organism and would not be among the remedies for the condition.

But the highest intensity wave for the above drugs given off by a culture or vaccine are feeble compared to the highest intensity wave for Koch. When a live organism is present I get a reaction on two rheostats. This has been proved again and again with cultures when the recognition number is hoisted twice. For instance, *Streptococcus rheumaticus*, if alive and active, gives a reaction on 65,061 on two rheostats and in the body I get a positive reaction on both sides of the abdomen. If the organism is dead we get a reaction on one rheostat only ; this in the body represents dead toxic material which must be excreted.

If I get a reaction on two rheostats which gives a neutral reaction I have concluded from clinical experience that the live cells are full of the toxin caused by the body's reaction to the organism, but that the organism itself is dead or quiescent. Such a condition, if general, requires no vaccine, but if a vaccine is needed the indication of the presence of the live organism can be found elsewhere. The brain may show the toxic reaction and the liver the live organism.

I have of course only been able to work out recognition numbers for a certain number of the commoner forms of organism, though I have a few of the rarer forms in this country. Recognition of organisms is a help, firstly as an indication for treatment, secondly as a guide to the patient's condition before and after treatment, and thirdly as part of the total picture of the individual.

My usual procedure with a new case is to measure up the activity of various organs and glands, and then having found the weakest spot, i.e. the organ which is most out of balance, tune in for remedies, putting these into the circuit till the patient's general body tuning registers 49,000 ohms or normal in the secondary circuit and also registers 37,000 ohms or 37, which means the same thing.

Having obtained an indication for a certain number of remedies I have then an indication of the nature of the invading organisms I am likely to find ; further, I have an indication of the kind of make-up the patient has.

The sex centre in the brain is tested if the sex organs are not balanced, and also various centres mentioned in the chapter on the Aura. Previous conversation with the patient will have given one some idea of the special line of inquiry to be made, but routine testing gives an aid which settles questions which may have arisen in the mind when one started.

Some practitioners using Abrams' method consider that no previous information should be acquired before testing for fear of mental interference. Personally I have such trust in the results of testing that I rule out preconceived ideas unless the test corresponds, and I often find that where the patient has given a clear psychological indication for a certain drug this proves the best drug to give even if it does not tune up in the routine above described ; usually it does, but not always. Finally all remedies are tested on the aura, and this is my guide for use.

A physician's method of course reflects his own mind. My mind medically is a combination of orthodox research, Abrams and homœopathy. I hope all methods and schools later will become unified; I dislike separatists, though I may be a rebel against strict conventions.

A physician of any school of thought would get a definite conception of the patient's condition from the information that calcium was the main need of the patient. He would think of various catarrhal conditions, the possibility of the presence of tubercle and of lowered parathyroid activity. The need of silica would certainly give a picture of the general condition to a homœopath. Excess of uric acid would paint a picture for all. Excess of guanidin makes me feel certain I have to do with cancer or sarcoma or a very closely allied condition. The analysis made of the patient by finding out what his organs are doing, with certain metabolic changes and the presence of certain organisms and the drugs he needs, gives me a picture which I fill in by talking to the patient and examining him in the ordinary way of all physicians.

I add to this an examination of his aura. It is only by balancing up the total evidence that a fair view can be obtained of the whole personality.

I may get a reaction for *B. typhosus*; it does not follow the patient has enteric fever, he may merely have what is commonly called rheumatism, although his small intestines and Peyer's patches are affected. Testing by the Abrams method is not a substitute for common sense, it is merely an aid.

There are of course definite named diseases with certain definite cell-changes, but Nature does not always work along book lines. There are conditions not due to acquired syphilis, possibly not due even to an hereditary taint, in which a positive Wassermann test occurs. Such a condition can be caused by a long-continued invasion by bowel organisms. Abrams recognised that he might get a 55 reaction by which he recognised syphilis when what he termed auto-intoxication was present.

Clinically again and again I have found that one of the most important things to find out was what stage the patient was in; the actual organism mattered less than the depth of the invasion. Obviously skin trouble due to a parasite is less serious than skin disease due to syphilis, but they may be present together, or the condition may be due to bowel organisms. The only means I have at present to recognise the presence of syphilis is by getting an altered reaction for syphilinum on 88,037 or lueticum 72,323, preparations made syphilitic tissues.

A considerable amount of trouble has happened over the diagnosis of syphilis on the 55 reaction; similar trouble might disappear if a diagnosis of active or hereditary syphilis were made on the 88,037 ohms reaction, which is the highest intensity frequency for syphilinum. This reaction occurs not only in acquired and hereditary syphilis, but in a condition caused by prolonged intestinal toxæmia. Abrams recognised that his 55 test might be caused by what he called auto-intoxication, and I·think it is also generally recognised that a positive Wassermann can be caused by other conditions than syphilis. An 88,037 reaction due to syphilitic taint is normalised by blue light, but one due to *B. morgan* is normalised by red light. One cannot even be certain that 88,037 changing with blue means syphilis, but it points that way.

When, however, I get a two-rheostat positive reaction for syphilinum, this vaccine is almost always needed. No homœopath would hesitate to use this remedy if the symptoms pointed to it, whatever the pathology was due to. I shall enlarge on this under " Stages in Disease." To those who might object to having poisons put into them I will point out that in so doing no morbid material is introduced ; the physician is simply giving a certain electrical stimulation. Certainly a C.M. or 100,000 dilution can contain no actual material as we commonly use the term, though its effects are potent.

Book pictures of disease have their definite use for students and practitioners, but the older one gets the more one realises that Nature, and more especially human nature, varies so much that pictures of each patient show us an almost infinite variety, especially in chronic disease. In acute disease we do indeed get more definite types, but these vary with time and season. Influenza varies every year and the pictures of classic disease vary from those of our youth and in different countries. Smallpox is here very different from the same disease in the East. The same organisms may cause a very different drug picture in different persons in chronic cases. They may also, according to their situation or virulence, cause totally different symptoms, which is saying the same thing in another way.

I headed this chapter." Recognition of Diseased Conditions," but a truer title might be " Recognition of the Patient's Totality."

When a new method is started it always meets with hostility, partly because it is new, the language is new, and partly because of natural errors in the way it is presented. It takes years for a pioneer mind to understand his own subject and bring it within his own understanding, let alone that of those who have not studied it. When discussing this with my friend Dr. Wheeler he said, " When you get a reaction for ' malarian ' (a nosode made from malarial blood) must you insist that the patient has malaria or has had malaria ? Could not one view it this way ?   The soil is there, and if he got malaria he would have it very badly."

When I am working from a nosode like malarian which is made not from an organism but from its results in the body, I accept this view, especially if I obtain a neutral reaction. If, however, the reaction is positive I feel that the likelihood of the original infection being due to malaria is somewhat increased.   Practically it does not matter ; if the malarian nosode is indicated I give it.

Just as one recognised that 88,037 might indicate a condition due to intestinal toxæmia as well as to syphilis, so one must recognise that 38,150 may be due to malaria, or there may be some other cause for the production of an altered compound which 38,150 represents.

When I get reactions which are positive for organisms which I have measured as separate entities apart from soil, I feel more certain about the indication.   One must, however, keep the door open for further knowledge.

CHAPTER XIV

STAGES IN DISEASE

A NY theories I have arrived at in regard to disease have been arrived at from practical points in treatment. In cases in which I did not get the amount of success I expected I found that I had not discovered the underlying cause.

This was sometimes due to not having looked for it and sometimes due to masked reactions. All Abrams' followers recognise this possibility in the case of tubercle which may be masked by the presence of staphylococci. Similarly the cancer virus may be masked. From a practical point of view it has been necessary to try and form an idea of what are the relative positions of diseased conditions, what is the earliest stage, and what are the end results.

Macdonagh, who has written several large volumes on the " Nature of Disease," and dwells on the likenesses between all diseases, considers, I gather, that there is really one disease in many stages. He places cancer as Nature's last ditch of defence and a staphylococcal infection of the skin as a very early manifestation of disease. With this I agree, but the question arises as to how I should group the intervening stages.

I have drawn up my tables of successive stages from practical experience in treatment. I place the end result first because my clinical experience has unfolded the scheme in that order.

I.	Cancer and sarcoma virus present.	
II.	Virus toxins present.	
III.	(a) Syphilinum stage. Thickening of tissues due to various flora.	(b) Medorrhinum s t a g e. Thinning out of tissues due to various flora.
IV.	Tubercle.	Tubercle.
V.	Septic and bowel organisms. Various conditions of depth penetration.	Catarrhal and bowel organisms. Erysipelatous condition.
VI.	Skin and mucous membranes infected by cocci or by coli.	Coli stage.
VII.	Toxic stage.	Toxic stage.
VIII.	Pretoxic stage.	Pretoxic stage.

I have divided the stages into two columns : (A) syphilinum stage, (B) medorrhinum stage. Under (A) I include not only real syphilis, but also a condition for which the syphilinum vaccine or nosode made from syphilitic tissues is a suitable remedy.

The homœopath will understand the term "syphilinum condition," but others may not. I cannot substitute the term positive Wassermann condition, for I am not sure that this always corresponds, though it does in some cases. The condition connotes a considerable thickening of tissues and altered gland conditions described later, one of the remedies for which is the syphilinum nosode. The condition follows long-continued irritation : this last factor must be stressed as a condition, for sometimes following the shock of an accident in which a bone has been broken a condition occurs in which syphilinum expedites recovery. Pseudo-syphilitic condition might be a better term.

From my special point of view, ignoring traditional terms, I should call it a condition of concentration of lesser degree than is found in cancer, in which some dispersal agent was needed.

This syphilitic or pseudo-syphilitic condition may follow a long-continued irritation by syphilitis toxins or by bowel organisms, or septic organisms.

When I have been treating cancer with a virus vaccine I have frequently had to follow this up with syphilinum, after which I have sometimes had to give tuberculinum and later vaccines for various bowel organisms or streptococcal vaccines or remedies to deal with these conditions. Abrams stated that if there was no syphilis present there was neither cancer nor tubercle. Substituting the term syphilinum condition for syphilis I agree as regards cancer, but as regards tubercle I do not agree, for I regard the tuberculinum stage as an earlier one than the syphilinum one.

I have had a number of cases where a tuberculin vaccine or corresponding drugs were needed to correct it, where there was no indication for syphilinum or corresponding treatment.

It is true that in many cases where tubercle has been present for some time syphilinum is needed and tubercle may be grafted on a syphilitic soil.

When I have given tuberculinum either primarily or following syphilinum I have had to follow this up by giving vaccines, nosodes or drugs to deal with what is called intestinal toxæmia, and finally to deal with the *B. coli* or staphylococci stage.

In the (A) condition we have then a final stage of large-cell masses in cancer, a lesser mass thickening in syphilis or pseudo-syphilis, involving many tissues, and again in some forms of tubercle a tendency to mass formations in tissues and glands.

The cell concentration also occurs with streptococcal organisms and bowel organisms, especially B. *proteus* and Morgan.

In the (B) group which ends with a condition needing medorrhinum, a nosode made from gonorrhœal tissues, there is a tendency to thinning-out of tissues, in some cases affecting bone—then an X-ray photo shows the bone which is affected translucent compared to those not affected. Such a condition may follow true gonorrhœa or organisms of the Neisserian group, such as Peterson's micrococcus or other catarrhal organisms.

I have frequently got the reaction for gonococci in persons who have never suffered from gonorrhœa, just as I have got B. *typhosus* in joints of persons who have never had an attack of acute enteric. Whether these modified forms would produce acute clinical gonorrhœa at first contact may be doubted, but organisms not only change their form but change in virulence.

Just as non-syphilitic organisms may lead up to the need for syphilinum, so may organisms which have no direct connection with gonorrhœa lead up to the need for medorrhinum, a diluted product of gonorrhœal tissues.

The stages in (B) class are similar. Medorrhinum has to be followed up by treatment for bowel and catarrhal organisms.

B. *coli* is often the last organism to be treated for in (A) class, and also is sometimes the last in (B). Whether both classes develop from B. *coli* I am not sure, but I think it is probable.

Certainly after expelling Morgan and typhosis coli one often has to treat B. *coli* just before the case arrives at the stage where only toxins are found, and no vaccine or corresponding high potency is needed, but merely 6-c. doses to secure elimination. In some cases after this there is a stage where no toxin can be detected and only a tissue remedy or colour is needed.

The above evidence of conditions has been gained from treatment of severe conditions leading to slighter conditions.

It is easy to understand that when organisms have been present they leave toxins behind, but it is perhaps less easy to understand how toxins can be present before organisms occur.

Evidence of this cannot be obtained from patients as a rule, but Nature has a way of building up just in the way she breaks down, and believing this I have been on the look-out for the first breaking-down stage, the pretoxic, and the second, the toxic. Examining myself, staff and household frequently, I have been able to examine these stages and let them develop naturally. I will describe my own case. I have a tendency to grow *B. typhosus* and *B. morgan.* I was an ambulant typhoid at school. Certain signs indicate to me that I need a dose of anacardium 6-c. I feel that nobody can move quite fast enough for me, I want to get along with the work immediately and express myself in action, and to use expletives with a bit of zip in them. When I test in a sufficiently early stage there is a reaction for anacardium 6-c. If I take a dose nothing more happens. If I leave things alone I get shortly an indication of *B. typhosus* toxins, and later the active organisms. With Morgan as a pure culture I am not stimulated to action, I feel sluggy, and here sulphur is the drug. The process of development is the same, the reactions are in order of sequence : sulphur[6]—Morgan neutral reaction indicating toxins, Morgan positive indicating active Morgan.

If you regard a toxin as necessarily a product of organisms we must use another word, but I use the word as a cell product and I have plenty of evidence that soil preparation takes place before invasion.

I think that what takes place is this : fatigue, or wrong feeding, changes in temperature, exposure, or depressing mental causes, change our cell chemistry and this causes an excretion into the gut which changes *B. coli*, always present, into some other form ; electrical attraction causes the penetration of the gut by the altered forms.

In fact the soil grows the organisms for which it is suitable, but soil changes take place first. This is what appears to happen in the garden and the farm.

This is not the place to argue whether bacteria are causes or concomitants of disease. The onset of acute disease after contact with persons who are discharging organisms looks as if the organism was a necessary part of the business, but as regards soil changing first I think we must consider that this happens in every case. A doctor in good form will mix up with every kind of infection and not get it, but when he gets fagged out he gets the trouble. Cold and fatigue may alter soil rapidly. A bad shock may do so also. I have measured this. Whether loss of resistance occurs quickly or slowly there must be a suitable soil or organisms are killed off.

(II) Inherited disease appears to be due to the presence of toxins, not organisms. This is not confined to what are termed venereal diseases. I have not had the opportunity to examine new-born infants, but I have found malarian toxins present in a patient who had never had the opportunity of incurring infection, and afterwards got the history that her father had a severe attack of malaria just before conception.

MacRoberts has worked out a certain level of toxins which is necessary before the corresponding organism can grow, and if these toxins are circulating in the mother's blood the child is certain to be affected. The results may not show for years and may be eliminated. I have evidence tending to show that a mild form of hereditary syphilis may show no result at all till the thirties, but it then shows when some strain occurs. Some of us, at any rate, start life in the toxic stage.

The tendency in some families to certain diseases shows that there is probably altered chemistry at birth. Shock or worry during pregnancy can act as a toxin to mother and child.

(III) The action of the internal secretory glands is also a sign of the stage the disease has reached.

As I shall show in the chapter on Cancer, there is over the growth the signs of a high intensity for some of the glands, either the local cells attract the hormones or there is locally a factory for similar cell products. In syphilis parathyroid and usually some other gland is found present in excess at the site of the lesion. In tubercular disease I have only found parathyroid present in excess locally, all other glands being deficient, in some cases lower than the activity in the gland itself.

This does not always happen in tubercle ; in some cases where the disease seems to be getting the upper hand parathyroid is lowest at the site of the highest infection.

I have yet to do a lot of work on this subject, but I have done enough to get a strong impression that an excess of gland supply in a lesion is an attempt at cure.

In the chapter on Internal Secretions I described the effect of glands on the activity of micro-organisms ; parathyroid came second in the list. It is not only in tubercle I have found its frequency give a high intensity over the lesion— this occurs with Morgan and streptococcal infections.

Pancreas was even more effective than parathyroid. This was surprising till I remembered the secondary effects in diabetes ; in the Madras Medical Department glycosuria was common and we had to make it a practical rule in the Surgeon-General's office that glycosuria without a tendency to carbuncle or some similar trouble was not a claim to special consideration for appointment to an easy post.

I have increasing evidence that one can get an idea of the stage reached by what the glands are doing.

To draw true conclusions a lot more work is needed, but the

picture unfolded in the chapter on Cancer is only one point of view ; it may give point to the view that cancer, like inflammation, is primarily a defence action, but the practical point is to give the gland which is the best defence medium or some vegetable substitute.

It is necessary for good results to obtain evidence as to the stage reached not only in the above classification, but also the stage of resistance or failure at the immediate stage reached, and gland observations assist me in this. When Nature is failing to make an effort due to exhaustion of certain elements, we must supply them.

CHAPTER XV

INFLAMMATORY DISEASE

THERE are two forces acting throughout the cosmos. One tends to drive matter towards the centre of a system, the other is dispersive and drives matter to the periphery.

These forces act in the atoms of our body ; the centralising force gets the upper hand in cancer ; in inflammatory disease the dispersive force is the stronger. If you look at the chart in the chapter on Cancer you will see that in cancer the majority of atoms measured on their atomic weights representing nucleæ intensity are above the normal line, whereas in the case of lobar pneumonia the majority of atoms are below the normal line. A corresponding chart was made measuring the atoms on their negative side on atomic numbers ; here the pneumonia case showed that the electronic or negative side was greatly increased in intensity.

In inflammatory conditions the general body tuning is increased on the negative side and diminished on the positive. The reverse occurs in cancer.

There is one element which I think invariably is an exception to this rule : free electrons of hydrogen are increased in cancer and diminished in inflammation. In cancer this increase in the free hydrogen electrons is accompanied by an acid condition with a decrease of the alkaline reserve. This condition of dispersion or concentration is one of the most important facts in disease ; a balance between these forces means health, the extreme of one over the other means death. When one is daily working to secure balance and sees how an excess of one force or the other threatens the existence of the human system, one feels sceptical of any theories about the cosmos being correct which show an entire victory for one force over the other. In our little cosmos, the human body, long-continued dispersion calls forth forces which tend to correct this and eventually overdo it unless checked.

To control these two forces we need agents which have the effect of dispersers or contractors.

If a substance will act as a disperser on the atom it will do this either in the human body or out of it.

At one point in my research I found that gentian and potato-eye both acted as dispersers in low potency. I found that this was caused by their phosphorus content. I tried phosphorus, the 15th element, on a considerable number of elements and found that in each case, when measured in my circuit, it caused a diminution of nuclei energy measured on the atomic weight and that it increased the free circulatory electron energy measured by the atomic number of the element. I then found that this important property was shared by the 13th element, aluminium ; the 14th, silica ; the 16th, sulphur ; and the 17th, chlorine ; so long as they were in low potency the 6-c dilution being the most effective.

The use of this discovery is not confined to cancer ; in syphilis, to a lesser extent in tubercle, and in some old chronic inflammatory conditions on the way to cancer, dispersers are needed. Wherever there are hardened masses to be softened and absorbed one of these dispersal agents will be needed either as an element or as a compound.

Nature seldom draws hard and fast lines as disease progresses, the tendency towards concentration increases, unless the original dispersal force has killed the patient.

Now what can we use for concentration ? To begin with, these five elements in high potency, a C.M. or M.M. dilution, act in this way. As often happens, a low or high potency acts in different directions.

I sought for some time, trying one element after another in low dilution or as a solid, to find a group of elements which would act as contractors. My efforts were not rewarded till I thought of the effect of the old homely remedy of a cold compress for a sore throat, made more effective by being covered with a stocking or scarf.

I tried the effect of placing water in the circuit—nothing happened. I then remembered that a bad head was relieved quicker by adding some spirit. I shook up some water with spirit and found that with this mixture I got the effect of concentration of the atom.

Spirit alone had no effect. What had happened ? Oxygen had no effect by itself ; there remained hydrogen.

I measured the intensity of hydrogen in tap-water, this = 23,333 ohms. After the spirit and water had been shaken up. Hydrogen = 111,111 when measured on 1-ohm tuning. Some hydrogen electrons had been set free.

Why does water act by itself over an inflammatory part ? The heat vaporises the water and the free electrons of hydrogen are attracted to the part where the hydrogen electrons are low and the hydrogen nuclei energy is high.

Consider another homely remedy for inflammation caused by wasp or bee stings—washing soda. This has the formula NO_2, CO_3, 10 H_2O. In the circuit melting crystals of soda acted as a condenser. For instance the atomic weight number of sulphur by itself measured an intensity of 43,333 ohms. When soda was added it measured 111,111 ohms. When applied to the site of a sting it will act as water acts on a sore throat and gives off hydrogen electrons.

Experiments showed that nitrogen, oxygen and carbon had no effect.

Traditional effective remedies all have a scientific basis if we look for it.

Part of the effect of dielectric oil, which is a hydro-carbon, is no doubt due to the same cause.

I then found that by charging the circuit with the oscilloclast set at 1 ohm I could get the same concentration effect when the setting of the machine gave 1 ohm with negative polarity.

I got the same effect with 172 ohms. As I said before, 1, and 172, the alpha and omega of the human atomic table have similar effects.

The numbers 13, 14, 15, 16 and 17 with negative polarity acted as dispensers, also the numbers 157, 158, 159, 160, and 161 acted as dispersers.

Numbers 13 to 17 in the third period correspond to 157 to 161 in the tenth period. See the human atomic table.

If the machine action was reversed so that these figures gave a positive polarity these numbers acted as concentrators.

The action of the oscilloclast on corresponding numbers to elements shows that the effect is a mathematical one.

It is futile to argue that the ohm and atomic numbers cannot correspond, because the ohm is supposed to be an arbitrary measure, when clinical and experimental effects show that 16 ohms correspond with the effect of sulphur, 17 ohms with chlorine, 1 ohm with hydrogen. Abrams' original treatment numbers with the oscilloclast were purely empirical, but I can see why a 1-ohm setting was effective in simple staphylococcal infections which are an early stage in inflammatory disease. In such a condition hydrogen electrons are wanting and we find in early inflammation that our simple remedies of supplying hydrogen are often effectual.

In the early stage of a mild cold or influenza, a hot bath followed by a good strong whiskey and hot water, and a purge, may be all the treatment that is needed to restore balance. But as matters progress more is needed ; more potent stimuli are necessary.

Between acute inflammation in an early stage and cancer there are a variety of stages in which we have to balance forces of expansion and concentration.

Inflammatory disease is characterised by the general body tuning being predominantly negative, the positive tuning is below 49,000, the norm. This is explained by the excess of negative electrons over protons. Affected organs measure below 37 ohms as a rule, though the internal secretory glands may measure above normal as in hyperthyroidism. There are in all diseases two conditions to be dealt with, one is a reduced rate of vibration of the affected organs and glands, the second is an increased rate of vibration due to the presence of micro-organisms or toxins. To secure balance both conditions must be treated. The invaders must be killed and organs of the body raised to normal vibration. The investigation of disease by means of measured vibrations is still in its early childhood. At present I can measure up organs and structures and see whether they are up to normal or above, and ascertain if certain organisms of which I have obtained specimens are present. In the meantime our ideas in regard to disease are changing ; we are not so certain about micro-organisms causing disease as we were. Some hold the view that microscopic organisms are merely concomitants, the true villains are ultra-microscopic viruses. This merely shifts the blame to something we cannot see even with a microscope. What is certain is that soil is the important factor ; neither microscopic organisms or virus can grow in a soil that is unfavourable to it. In the meantime it is worth while searching for the flora which do flourish in the blood-stream as their presence or absence gives us indications for treatment and a means of judging progress. It is impossible to deal with many examples of inflammatory disease ; one phenomenon common to over 90 per cent. of chronic cases is intestinal toxæmia.

The alimentary tract is the place where we grow a variety of organisms, and when these are absorbed trouble follows. Why do we encourage certain organisms and not others ? Because we have a certain kind of soil. What makes our soil ? Heredity, environment and our thoughts. There are two fear organisms, *B. gaertner* and *B. proteus*. If we can expel them we assist the psyche and give it time to recover. *B. gaertner* occurs more often in women and is accompanied often by shaking fits ; fear in this case is a vague dread from no ascertainable cause : the family misfit often has *gaertner*. *B. proteus* occurs more often in men and the fear which goes with it can be attributed to some definite cause, though this may be imaginary or there may be some basis of reality which has become exaggerated. Mental strain produces such an invasion. A number of civilians used to business strains changed their intestinal flora during the war ; fear of death, unusual responsibility, unusual discipline, upset their nervous systems referred to as neurasthenia. A number of these were Proteus cases. " Peter Jackson," cigar merchant, was a typical case. On the other hand, open-air men in the Services after the War had to earn their living in civil life, and the altered strains again produced Proteus. There is one organism very few doctors know about, that is *B. bachii*. It has a special affection for the heart. Those who suffer from it often have odd heart symptoms : their hearts squeak, they get electric shocks, they get feelings as if a banjo string had been twanged inside them, vibrations in the street affect the heart. The cultural reactions of *B. bachii* are :—

Glucose	Lactose	Cane sugar	Dulcite
Acid, gas.	Nil.	Acid, gas.	Acid, gas.

B. bachii is a close relation of the paratyphoids. Some asthma cases grow *B. bachii*. The non-lactose fermenting organisms are not harmless as has been stated, they are the commonest concomitants of troubles which vanish when we are rid of them. *B. typhosus* is very common in chronic cases ; the paratyphoids less so.

It appears to be dangerous to tell a patient he is absorbing typhoid and paratyphoid. He goes and tells his doctor he has typhoid in spite of being told it is chronic, and the doctor says indignantly there is no sign of typhoid or paratyphoid. Apparently a large number of the medical profession are ignorant that almost any organism can accompany either acute or chronic symptoms. Typhosus is common as a cause of joint affection. I sometimes find tetanus in cases of occasional spasm. It is probably this mild form which occasionally becomes serious after an operation and causes death and general consternation and trouble.

Every alteration from normal causes certain chemical changes ; as research goes on more indications will be found for the recognition of specific conditions—those which have been found will be checked up.

The 450-ohm reaction for blood-pressure which is accompanied by diminution of pepsin is certainly a reliable indication of change in pressure but not always accurate ; a swinging balance either way may occur in high blood-pressure, too much 450 ohms, whatever that may indicate, may have the

same effect as too little.   This phenomenon is a common one
after a dose of a drug which has caused a reaction.   Symptoms may be increased in severity and the frequency by
which the drug is recognised will register below 37 instead
of above it.   Removal of the thyroid will produce symptoms
resembling hyperthyroidism which cannot be due to excess
of thyroid.   A considerable amount of evidence can be
collected by measuring known compounds on their molecular
weights and these in excess give a double-positive reaction ;
in extreme deficiency they give a double-negative = 74.   Any
substance which can be isolated can have its highest intensity
frequency taken and can therefore be recognised later even
if its correct chemical formula be unknown.   A great deal
more can be done to elucidate the problems of the human
body by chemistry, but we must remember it is merely
chemistry and merely one link in the chain of evidence ;
when we have found excess of uric acid or what not this is
not the disease.   The real disease may be some lesion in
the psyche, for instance, asthma may be due to want of
spiritual freedom, or shall we say suitable mental atmosphere.

ASTHMA AND ALLIED CONDITIONS.

Certain individuals show an oversensitiveness to external
stimuli ; this appears to be inherited, for it runs in families ;
different members of the family will suffer from asthma, hay
fever, urticaria, fits, or they may show signs of, we will say,
mental nettlerash.

This last class will jump at noises, start if touched, are
ticklish, they are easily offended, weep easily, they may enjoy
music and colour more than others, but they are too sensitive
in every way to mental or physical stimuli.   With such cases
think of nat. mur. 30, which is a contractor, and give it continuously for a period, or give at wider intervals nat. mur. 200
or higher.

The nettlerash folk may be so sensitive that they get a
rash from their own hair when it is cut.   Asthma, with its
typical attacks of difficulty in breathing, is one of the symptoms
of the condition.   Attacks of shortness of breath like asthma
may be due to other causes, such as local irritation of nerves
connected with respiration.

I do not think that there is any true division between what
is called cardiac asthma and the bronchial kind.   Only the
different tissue or nerve centres are affected.   A considerable
number of asthmatics are sensitive to hair or feathers or the

non-hæmolytic streptococcus or foodstuffs of certain kinds. These folk have in them an unbalanced molecule which gives a frequency on 88,897 ohms tuning. This body is present in hens' eggs in great intensity. In the whites of eggs I find that 88,897 gives a negative reaction equal to 34,444 ohms and a positive reaction equal to 85,555 ; in the yolk these figures are reversed and balance the figures of the white ; hence the egg as a whole is balanced positively and negatively.

I obtained this item of knowledge by putting preparations of the following substances in the circuit together and taking a common denominator wave. I give the personal rate for each substance and group :—

Animal hair	..	..	38,987	Sheep	..	..	87,633
Horse hair	..	..	87,682	Feathers	..	..	88,879
Dog hair	..	..	87,871	Goose	..	..	88,851
Rabbit fur	..	..	87,682	Chicken	..	..	88,767
Guinea-pig	..	..	87,742	Duck	..	..	88,778
Cat hair	..	..	46,589				

If the above substances are introduced into the circuit with a normal blood and a reaction is taken, the most prominent displaced wave is 86,241, which is the P.R. for sabadilla, and sabadilla is a drug which is most useful in these cases and which I have had occasion to give in asthma and hay fever with good effect. It is a recognised remedy for hay fever. If the patient is suffering from any of the above reactions we can at once spot what is affecting him. Heart and lungs are not the only parts affected ; spasm of any muscular tube may be involved, for instance, the vagina. In such a case search especially for a mental connection and try the effect of secale, a dilution of ergot.

In all cases of asthma it is of course necessary to look for surgical or osteopathic lesions which need attention by appropriate means. It is futile to be treating the higher centres if grosser reasons exist for the condition. It is a moot point when such treatment should take place. Each case must be treated in conjunction with the selected colleague. Asthma is due to a most complicated mechanism, but we can simplify things to a certain extent by finding out the exciting causes and giving appropriate remedies. In general, each case must be treated on indicated drugs according to symptoms or frequencies.

All glands are affected in these cases, but the gland extracts which I have found in experiments and in practice to be effective are first, ovarian residue, which increases deficient hæmoglobin and 88,897, then bone-marrow, thirdly pitocin, and then adrenalin and pineal or thymus. Other glands in whole or part were useless or harmful. A gland preparation corresponding to ovarian residue is needed for men. Special attention is needed to liver function. Bodies are found in the urine which Fehling's solution precipitates but which do not produce the ordinary effect when sugar is present. The Abrams reaction for asthma was 29, which is the atomic number of copper. Copper is a recognised remedy for asthma. If a copper reaction is present it is due to toxins in the liver.

Asthma is also closely connected with intestinal toxæmia and this must be treated. Those who treat with the oscillo-clast should treat over the heart-lung centre, half-way between the left nipple and the centre-line of the body. The abdominal centre also should have attention in the middle line, about halfway from navel to sternum.

It takes a long time to alter a person's make-up, but it can be done, especially if they are ready to follow directions and can remove from their environment provocative substances such as hair, feathers, living or dead, and strictly avoid irritating forms of food.

CHAPTER XVI

TREATMENT

I.

THERE are five principles in the treatment of a sick person which are most important to keep in mind.

The first is that we treat the whole individual as a living unit. The homœopaths lay stress on this point : they seek to find the similimum for the whole patient and lay considerable stress on mental symptoms. Ordinary medical textbooks give but little hint of such an idea. They discuss how to treat particular conditions under named diseases, but rarely suggest that there is an all-embracing whole which needs attention.

I sometimes find that patients have been treated by a series of specialists with no physician to co-ordinate the line of treatment. It ought not to need saying that if one important organ is out of order the whole body suffers. A conscientious lady said to me that as she was away from her own doctor I might treat her ear, but I must not treat herself, as that would not be loyal to her London doctor. Owing to the attitude of the bulk of the profession, a large number of the public imagine that one organ can be treated by itself. I have no hesitation in saying that that is always wrong. Even if glasses are needed, the whole body should be treated as well. Eye-strain may be a very important item, and may call for the oculist's aid, but it is often a great saving of time and expense to treat the whole condition first. Some children need glasses very early in life, but even here there is probably some condition which needs correcting in the whole body.

Does a fracture of a bone need medical treatment ? Undoubtedly, for you cannot break a bone without shock to the whole system, and the bone will heal quicker if symphytum or arnica is given. We are but slowly learning that the body politic is one, and no nation can suffer without all suffering ; no wonder we are slow to realise that no one part of the body can suffer without the whole of the body suffering. Abrams' genius has enabled us to see this clearly. For if, as he has shown, it is possible to find out what is happening in various parts of the body by examining a little blood or serum, it becomes evident that the whole body is affected by what happens to the part.   For example, a drop of blood from a person with a fracture will give an altered reaction for bone and usually a reaction for symphytum.   I obtained such a reaction from a colleague and this led to his having an X-ray taken, which showed a fractured fibula, which he had not realised had been fractured.

All my work makes me agree with the followers of Hahnemann that we must try to treat the patient as a whole.   I do not wish to suggest that the larger part of the profession never does this.   I believe a number do, but I feel sure that this first principle in healing is not sufficiently attended to. I believe that this treatment of the individual was really better attended to when people went year after year to the same family doctor ; when folk moved about less, and were attended by a man who had known them from childhood. The young practitioner is inclined to sneer at the old-fashioned man, who the patients say understands their constitution and who has stuck in one place all his professional life ; but many of these older folk had some sound ideas, not learnt at the hospital school but in the school of life.

(I) I have mentioned mental symptoms and have dealt in detail elsewhere with the importance of the psyche.   Let us consider why mental symptoms are so important in deciding what remedies to give.   Even if it is not conceded that man is a spiritual being, it is generally admitted that mind determines much of our physical make-up and makes us differ so much from one another.   We are all of us made of the same compounds from a chemical point of view.   In matter, we are practically the same.   Mentally, or I prefer to say spiritually, for it is the ego that actuates the whole unit, we are very different.

Homœopathic works classify under each drug a special type of mental character attributed to the person who needs that drug.   I have found this very useful in a number of cases, but my trouble in regard to this subject is that our bodies and characteristics are so complicated that seldom does one drug cover the whole ground, either in the picture drawn in the books or in my findings in testing.   Clinically, a patient may need arsenic and she may give the characteristics of arsenic mentally, but she may also need iron or cadmium sulph. A patient may need sulphur and also tin and show signs of needing both mentally.   I have the advantage of testing, and I test out all remedies on the aura.   A person who shows signs of needing arsenic mentally will grow organisms con-

nected with arsenic, such as *B. proteus*. A person who shows
calcium mental symptoms encourages all the catarrhal
organisms.

The sick mind may be regarded as the result of the sick
body, or the sick body as the result of the sick mind, but the
fact remains that certain mental types grow certain kinds of
organisms. I have lately been finding a modified type of
glanders organism in people who are too fat and need calcium
carbonate. Getting fat goes with a certain type of mind.
Caesar preferred that type of senator. But all fat people are
not the same, and all of them may not need calc. carb. There
is the sepia type : sepia, the inky fluid of the cuttlefish,
contains calcium, but how different is the type. Very few
sepias can be fat, they are too restless, too agitated, too
unhappy. Sepias grow Gaertner.

To cure a patient, not only the chemical body but layers of
the personality which makes up the whole individual must
be treated. This is no fancy, for I can measure them, and
unless you have thumbs instead of fingers you can test it
yourself. Some day these layers will be named and their
functions tested out. In the meantime I know they correspond to some reality other than chemical. Results are much
better since I have worked on the biomorphs as a final test
for treatment. If life forces are adequately and correctly stimulated the chemistry of the body is corrected by them. It
is more important to realise the mental type of the patient
than anything else.

(II) The second principle in treatment is to pay attention
to detail and know the root-cause of the trouble before deciding
on what is the best treatment for the whole individual. Perhaps the best phrase to express this in terms of my own method
is " close tuning."

Here we see the other side of the shield. It seems to me
that many of Hahnemann's followers with their wonderful
knowledge of remedies are very apt to ignore detailed pathology. I do not say this from observation of any laxity on
the part of any individual, but from the general trend of
articles in the journals. At any one moment it may be very
essential to pay special attention to a certain organ. Life
itself may depend on relief of a specific condition, or the
patient's comfort may demand relief of a particular symptom.

Orthodox medicine has a long list of heroes who have devoted
their lives to research on the pathology of certain diseases
and to their relief.

The ground to be covered is beyond the scope of any one

individual ; at three-score years one can only feel very humble at one's own ignorance, and endeavour by constant study to help oneself and, incidentally, others who choose to avail themselves of anything one may add to the general knowledge. The only way to learn is to keep an open mind and utilise any piece of knowledge that one may pick up, and, if possible, expand it.

To secure " close tuning " I find it necessary to examine the condition of balance of each organ, to discover the stage the disease has reached : does it correspond with the syphilinum stage or tubercular, has it involved bone or the nervous system? I then work from the weakest point found. Here will be found all the organisms which are present in the body. To deal with these I seldom use vaccines made from organisms unless I get a total vaccine made from the whole secretion. Selection of one or two organisms from sputa or a stool or discharge is far less effective than using the whole secretion, if it be of a nature which can be used. Whole sputa, for instance, when potentised gives the patient not only his organisms but his soil. If I use this I give a series of doses at 30-c. Far more frequently I use a cm. or mm. of a drug or drugs which will deal with all the organisms found. In many cases of tubercule there is a syphilinum condition ; the remedies which will deal with the tubercle are not always effective with this, therefore I give syphilinum plus either crotalus or naja or lachesis or one of the more active vegetable poisons in the form of an mm. or cm. If streptococci be present probably a snake remedy is needed. " Close tuning " indicates dealing with all the organisms present or trying to do so. The orthodox homœopath will only give one dose or one drug. Perhaps he is right when he cannot test, but when one can test there is no sense in leaving organisms to flourish for sake of a theory. According to the severity of the case I give one, two or more doses of the high potencies found necessary to deal with the organisms present which cause a vibration above normal. There remains to give concomitant remedies to bring the organs which are vibrating below normal up to their normal rate. In the case of glands it may be a useful measure to supply some material for the body to work up into gland material. This will be the gland with the lowest balance. I am indebted to Dr. Vannier of Paris for the idea of con- comitant drugs. A concomitant drug has a wave in common with the condition it is given to relieve ; all tubercle elimina- tors give a wave corresponding to the kind of tubercle which it is desired to treat. This brings me to the third principle : elimination.

(III) We can hardly lay too much stress on elimination. How often is an attack of catarrh cured by the family physician (who may be the experienced mother of a family) by a hot bath and a warm stimulating drink which acts on skin and kidneys, and a brisk purge. The benefit of many of the spas is due to this eliminatory action. In practice I think the profession is ahead of medical textbooks. If one can select a suitable table water for the case it may well be used to assist elimination, but it should be chosen with care. I generally find that drinking plenty of hot water away from meals, with the specific concomitants I have hereafter indicated, is sufficient.

Every physician of experience who works carefully, could give cases where he had slipped up by too great eagerness in giving drugs that act as vaccines and paying too little attention to elimination. To manage a chronic case, such as advanced rheumatism or cancer, without getting complications, requires great care and patience. Again and again I have felt that we should have got along better had I gone more slowly. The patient and the doctor want results, and sometimes they get them in a way which is not pleasant.

Elimination means drainage : where there is pus let it out ; if a tooth is stopping drainage have it out, but make certain that it really has to go. Dead teeth are thoroughly bad teeth, life cannot be put into them and they have no real place in a person's economy except as a source of trouble and expense later on, much better have a place which can be cleaned. There is some hope for live teeth. You may get the surrounding tissues to clean up ; they are alive. Dead teeth cannot be made alive. In testing teeth remember that a live tooth will give a reflex through two rheostats on 70,269 ohms, the frequency for teeth.

Our art is to deal with live things ; dead things should be removed, not patched up. I have a great respect for the wonderful skill developed by the dental profession in saving our teeth and preserving the shape of the jaw instead of extracting wholesale as was the fashion at one time. Live teeth should, I am sure, be saved whenever possible, but I feel strongly that leaving in dead teeth is a wrong principle. No surgeon leaves in a bit of dead bone or dead tissue ; anything certain to die he removes.

Surgeons have, in the past, placed in the body all sorts of foreign bodies which cannot be absorbed. I believe this practice will be given up and replaced by better methods. A method may be perfect mechanically, but if untrue to life it must fail. I believe if everyone with decayed teeth was treated generally, many teeth that are now killed could be saved and the elimination of dead teeth would not be needed. So-called preservation of teeth by killing their nerves is, I am sure, bad practice and might in many cases be avoided if general treatment of the whole condition were undertaken. This may cause criticism by dentists ; it is written to stir up thought on the subject.

I say to electronic workers : Work in co-operation with others. When the surgeon-dentist is needed to secure drainage let him get to work in good time.

(IV) The fourth important point in treatment is dosage. This is nearly as important as giving the right drug. Not quite, for if you give too low a potency it does something ; it may not be much use, but Nature uses it in a beneficial way.

I have pointed out that drugs alter their effects in accordance with the state of solution they are in. If you give tincture of cinnamon when it is not much needed nothing very much happens, but if you give a cm. quite a lot happens and very quickly. I once tried it. I did not consciously wish to prove on my own person the effect of a high-potency cinnamon, but probably the unconscious mind wished to do so. A little while previously I had had a very unpleasant attack of influenza. *B. influenzæ* was present and probably other things. One cm. of cinnamon removed all pain in an hour or two. At the end of a fortnight's holiday on the Broads, cold and damp and perhaps a little over-exertion, brought on another attack. I repeated the remedy with success. Then a fortnight later the conscious mind said it was time to have another dose. This time I had all the classic signs of influenza : sore throat, pain in the back and limbs and complete misery, but it was cinnamon poisoning, not influenza, as I proved by testing. This was sufficient proof to me of the efficiency of homœopathic doses. The name has been used sometimes to indicate feeble ineffective doses. Once is sufficient for proving drugs in this manner.

If I want to prove a drug now I put it in my circuit and harness myself in. I can get sufficient evidence that way of its tendency.

In my youth I often sneered at the idea of the infinitesimal dose. I do so no longer. As a beginner in the use of dilutions I got some notable successes with varied doses. I will quote three : The first was a patient in great pain—agonising pain, he called it—a red patch over the left mastoid, a discharge from the left ear, temperature over 103°, and a very rapid pulse. I found a reaction for streptococcus and sulphur and found that a cm. of sulphur normalised the reactions. Next day he reported that he was out of pain within an hour. His temperature was then normal, pulse normal, red patch gone. Peroxide and gentle irrigation of the outer ear cured the case without further active treatment.

The next case was a young lady in pain owing to her period ; she had a severe headache and wept considerably. I found she had a much increased post-pituitary reaction and some intestinal absorption. I gave nat. mur. 12-c. Five days later she returned full of joy and thankfulness ; the pain had gone at once and she had thoroughly enjoyed her holiday. She seemed a totally different personality.

The third case was also a nat. mur. one. This was a lady in the forties who wept copiously on every occasion. I had previously cured a very unpleasant condition of her nose which was sufficiently bulbous to make her a prominent object wherever she went. I had worked her out as nat. mur. but did not seem to be able to improve the mental condition with either high or low doses. I consulted the late Dr. Frank Shaw of St. Leonards. He advised nat. mur. 30-c for fourteen days continuously. At the end of that time instead of a wet, moist, unpleasant body, a calm gracious person whom it was a treat to meet came to my consulting room.

As a rule, when the mental similimum can be diagnosed, the trouble can be cured.

I was a very young homœopath then, and had a lot of lessons coming to me. Now, all these cases acted in a more or less miraculous way, because the right does was given. Some require high potencies, some require mass doses, some do best on colloids. There is a right dose for everyone. I think I can say that I have never done much with a chronic case permanently without giving either a vaccine at 30-c repeated, or one or more really high potencies. In chronic cases the condition has been changing slowly for a long time ; to restore balance a powerful stimulus is needed at the start to turn the tide backwards.

There are conditions which may need doses of solids or tinctures, acute cases in which big doses are needed at short intervals for a very short period, chronic cases in which we get the reaction 74 — — for something indicating a great need for that substance. It often assists in these cases to give solids or very low potencies with a higher potency to stimulate the function which will induce the body to assimilate these substances. For instance in subthyroidism solid thyroid in very small doses is indicated, with a stimulator of the thyroid. Where we have had gross treatment inducing dispersion, as in the case of streptococcal vaccination I quoted, mass doses of calcium lactate are more quickly efficient than anything more refined.

Some of the members of my profession have curious prejudices. On the one hand a certain London medical society in 1929 insisted on doctors pledging themselves not to use homœopathic remedies before they were allowed to join. I do not think that at any period of my career such an idea as this would have entered my head. It is worthy of the Church in the Middle Ages. On the other hand a colleague of mine was consulted by a homœopathic practitioner in regard to a tapeworm ; male fern was suggested to him as the obvious remedy. The reply was, " It is against my principles to use mass doses ! " History does not relate what happened to the tapeworm—presumably it still flourishes.

When you get a low-down organism like a tapeworm, who does not appreciate the power of the infinitesimal dose, you have to use mass doses sufficiently toxic to dislodge him. My experience with threadworms is the same. Dilutions should be given to clear up the condition, but if you want rapid results give mass doses of santonin or naphthaline. For dealing with bacterial invasion and toxæmias I prefer dilutions high or low. For parasites I prefer doses which are immediately toxic to the parasite.

The use of drugs in enormous doses seems to me to be very risky and unnatural. I should like to know what happens later on after a dose of so much tinct. digitalis, per body-weight. Reports of immediate effects on the heart are good, but how long does it take to get rid of this mass of foreign material ?

My strong feeling is that results will show themselves later on. I have found them with other drugs given in far less quantities. This impulse to use things of enormous power is a form of materialism, an incapability to realise that the body is a delicate mechanism interleaved by the psyche on whom we really have to act. The physical home of the human spirit does not need to be treated as if it were an engineering proposition. This rage for the use of great physical force is all wrong. We should realise in time that the body needs the most tender treatment. What is really needed is accurate tuning, correct intensity of dose and removal of dead matter. We are dealing with radiating life, not a piece of dead mechanism.

(V) The fifth principle to be observed is attention to " function." The use of concomitant drugs or drainage remedies, or whatever one chooses to call them, in part secures this end. But drug treatment is only a part of medical treatment. There is a much wider application of the term function. I am not only thinking of stimulating organs by drugs or securing drainage in a surgical sense. I am thinking here of the use of the whole body, limbs, guts, sense organs, sex organs and mind. I have a hatred for splints, whether they are physical or mental. Of course there are times when you must wear splints, there are conditions where complete rest is needed. A cut tendon must be given an opportunity to heal before it can be used ; some injuries do require absolute rest. Life, however, means activity. Every thought produces chemical change. Thought causes the ebb and flow of life-forces as measured by the biomorphic frequencies. Immobility is absolutely an unnatural condition for a live body. A good many doctors become for one reason or another fearful old women in this matter. I know one man who put all his vaccination cases into slings. This kind of coddling is all wrong. It may pay the doctor in L.S.D., but it hurts the patient's morale. While I was out in India I saw a number of old fractures which certainly looked very ugly, but the limbs were perfectly useful. One man passed the recruiting officer who made him do physical jerks with his coat on. I rejected him on æsthetic grounds, as being an unpleasant sight on parade for physical drill, but he could have made a perfectly good soldier in every other way. We could afford to be particular then.

During the war I had every case I possibly could under the X-ray screen. One patient had one arm and both legs in splints. After viewing these I told him to put the other arm under the screen ; he objected. As there was a healed wound I insisted, and found a fractured radius ; this had joined up quite well without the use of a splint at all. The patient said he had not mentioned this wound as he was not going to lose the use of his cigarette hand. The arm in use was free of adhesions and useful. The arm on a splint took some time to function properly.

As I had charge of the Kitchener Hospital Orthopædic Department and two surgical blocks, I had the opportunity of seeing how different methods worked. All my own fracture cases were taken down frequently and massaged. No one was permitted to lose the use of a limb from want of attention to function. As soon as the bone was sufficiently united to keep straight, splints were taken off and electrical treatment

given. I used to tell my colleagues than the splint was more
terrible than the shell. In the orthopædic department we
spent months trying to undo the trouble caused by prolonged
splinting without movement. There are perhaps some cases
where absolute rest is needed, where nerves are damaged, as
in a badly dislocated elbow : then it should be absolute.
Mr. H. G. Buckingham, who is keen on ju-jitsu, tells me that
the Japanese instructors only allowed ten minutes off the mat
for a dislocation. Immediate use after replacement and
massage was a success.

In the Boxer Campaign I tore some back muscles badly
doing an exhibition fireman's lift on a member of the Sikh
tug-of-war team. My orderly got me right in a couple of
days by finding the sore place, standing on it, and then sliding
off. This was repeated before we started marching and
when we finished I was jumping on my pony the very next
day. The tear was so bad an hour or two after it occurred
that I could hardly get up the steps of the temple we were
quartered in. The Eastern system of massage includes
prompt use. The orthodox surgeon in Europe mainly relies
on rest—hence the incomes made by various unqualified
persons. For injuries two things should be kept in mind :
first function, second treatment of the general condition.

I was once asked to treat a lady whose body was encased
in a plaster jacket. I could not make out any pathological
condition that would account for this treatment except
muscular and mental floppiness. She had gradually been
built in, the splint-makers propped her up a bit on the right
and then she flopped left ; this was remedied and then she
flopped forward. Lying down she could move all her muscles,
but after a few minutes' moving about without her shell she
collapsed. She had become a complete mollusc, ruined body
and soul by splints.

Another ruinous form of splint is a large metal plate which
is pressed on to the abdomen to support muscles which should
be gradually trained by gentle exercises and electrical stimuli
to do their work. Such plates and even metal stay-busks
usually have a lowering effect on vital forces. A. E. Baines
cured a bad case of anæmia simply by inducing the patient
to leave off wearing metal in her stays. He found that her
stay-busks had become magnets and were affecting the iron
in her blood. Anything that checks function should be
dropped as soon as possible. The rising generation are doing
without stays, but they are using a lot of foreign material
to decorate (?) their lips and cheeks. It is sometimes necessary

to wire a patella or plate a fracture, but the wire or plate should be removed when the join is safely made before trouble occurs, instead of waiting for it.

The question of stoppings for teeth requires to be gone into. It is known that small electrical currents are sometimes set up and poisoning results. The probable line of safety is a finely-made amalgam which is neutral and remains neutral in the mouth. I would suggest a study of the chemistry of the teeth themselves. Safety is preferable to glitter. Quite possibly this has been done, but my method could be used to test combinations before they were put into teeth and special amalgams selected for certain patients, as effective tooth-stopping, like everything else, must vary for individuals.

I would lay down two sound rules :—

(1) Never introduce dead stuff into the body if you can avoid it. If you must leave it in permanently, be most careful in its selection for your patient.

(2) Remove all splints the first moment they can come off and train up muscles and joints by exercises. In a word, excite function.

Don't coddle children. Let them do things for themselves ; as few clothes as possible. I do not mean that children should be allowed to go blue with cold in this climate. All things in reason ! The Esquimo are a hardy race, but they wrap up to meet the climate.

Probably the hard time we are going through is a good thing for the rising generation. They have to learn to do things for themselves, help in the house, get out in the world earlier. It is no use coddling boys and girls morally. Teach them the facts of life, try to make them see that indulgence and general slackness are rotten. Teach them that they have their own bodies and spirits to look after. Everything has to be paid for sooner or later, but virtue due to the prison-house is of no use to anyone ; better learn the lessons of life early.

Of all the damned silly ideas that a nation every took up prohibition is the worst. We are nearly as silly in some ways. The American is run by school-marms in his youth and continues the habit. The sooner we get rid of all grandmotherly legislation the better. We want to be free—real *men* and *women* who are alive in every possible way. Free to choose between good and evil. There is too much bolstering up all round. The dole is acting as a curse and no one should get a single penny for doing nothing. Everything that lowers mental responsibility or lowers function of mind and body is bad. Real Socialism will mean organisation, so that if you don't work you starve. If nothing else can be found for you, you could clean litter in the parks and streets.

Function means to use everything. Most of our social services check rather than increase function. Education is faulty. Is the Public School boy taught to think for himself? No. He is taught good form, he is taught a number of things which are absolutely useless to him and he is stunted mentally. He is taught certain virtues of cleanliness, playing the game to a certain point, and being like everybody else of his class. He is not taught to think for himself, he is taught to look down on and dislike anyone who does think for himself. Original ideas only come out later on with difficulty, unless they are of the mistaken patholo gical sort that thinks vice and ugliness original. The Council School children are also taught a lot of stuff which is not needed.

The only education which is of any use at all aims at three things : character, learning to think, learning to do things. That is training spirit, mind and body.

We teach boys and girls to play ball games but not to use their fingers. We teach them a lot of dead languages they can't think in, but do not teach them to think for themselves. Col. R. H. Elliot invented a new operation for glaucoma. It was taken up all over the world before it took on in London. It will be used in London many years after some other treatment has been found better elsewhere. This is merely a sample of the intense slowness of the functioning of the English brain owing to faulty education. The Englishman has rather better brains than the rest of the world, but he is ashamed to use them. His public school, university, hospitals and other schools all conspire to keep him splinted. If you have not a free mind your spirit and body cannot act in unison.

We are full of fears : fear of not being correct, fear of being different, fear of being poor, fear of being thought a bit cracked. To be a materialist is a bit *démodé* but to be a spiritualist is far worse—most dangerous. Why not be natural and take an interest in all the jolly, lovely, horrible and interesting things in all the universe? What does it matter what people think? Enjoy life to the full. This cramping of life affects health. The people who have most fears grow Gaertner and Proteus and get cancer. Worry is the worst toxin there is. What is the worst worry? Fear of loss of position. Most people can cheerfully give up a few luxuries. They even feel better for walking instead of constant motoring ; but it is the fear of what others will think that is the worst worry. Useless expenditure on appearances and snobbery makes things worse. There is nothing that lowers vitality like fear, and a great deal of our fears are quite unnecessary. It is fear that is ruining business at the present time. If our civilisation goes under it will be on account of fear.

Fear holds up research. Many able men give up Abrams' methods owing to fear of their neighbours. They were made to understand that their ordinary practice would go if they indulged in unorthodox practices. Fear of the new thing is partly snobbery, partly a fear of the unknown, as persons fear death or spirits. Fear of death never holds it off ; it brings it nearer. Fear of real life cramps a number of people. I have known a number of women cramped and crippled mentally and bodily because they were not taught the ordinary physiology of conception and birth, mainly because they shirked learning. The fear of having children is cramping to health. I do not say that limitation of families is not neces- sary, but I do say that those who cannot accept risks cheerfully had better remain maids. If you cannot live freely and bravely in every way, you suffer in mind and body.

Every suppression means some loss if it is caused by fear ; if it be a free choice for the sake of true wisdom, it is a gain. Discipline of body, mind and soul is necessary. We must be captains of our souls, not because we fear, but because we want to gain power and fuller life.

It may seem that this outburst on freedom has not much to do with my particular work. It has a vast deal to do with it, for I have measured up these fears and their results. The realities of fear are beyond speech. They poison life. I have lived through them and I know. It is the view of a freer and better existence soon to come which has very largely freed me. But we can be free here, as well as there, in spite of cramping bodies.

HOMŒOPATHY.

There are two main principles in the homœopathic views of medicine. The first is the most important : to select the drug which is the best as representing the whole patient. The simillimum. This is the drug which when given in excess would cause a similar group of symptoms to those of the patient. This principle is generally understood in the term " a hair of the dog that bit you." The use of vaccines has made the idea familiar and understandable.

This principle has been discussed and illustrated over and over again with much better knowledge than I can contribute.

The second principle of the use of the small dose or the infinitesimal dose as given in high potencies does not appear to have been explained. Writers merely appeal to experience. Here I can make a contribution and suggest an explanation.

The use of the infinitesimal dose has caused great merriment ; those who have not tried it have regarded the use of great dilution as a proof of the inherent absurdity of homœopathy.

The work done on the study of the atom of late years must make all thoughtful people less certain of their assumption that high dilutions are necessarily absurd.

My conversion to the use of high dilutions occurred during the course of my research on drugs. I found that a reaction for copper in a cancer case was normalised when a copper electrode was held at a distance of about three feet over the testing set, but no great effect took place when the electrode was placed on the rheostats. Action from a distance was obviously equivalent to dilution. Clinical trial converted me to the use of dilutions both high and low.

Homœopathic dilutions, or potencies, as they are called in England, are made in a tenth or a hundredth series. One part of the substance, say silica, is grown up with 9 or 99 parts of sugar of milk ; from this mixture one part is taken and ground up with 9 or 99 parts of sugar of milk. Some firms do this a dozen times, some half a dozen times, and further dilutions are made with alcohol. High dilutions are now made by machinery.

I once tested out a series of preparations, some of which had been ground twelve times and some six, and then diluted with alcohol to 30 dilutions. I could discover no difference in the result.

The tenth series is written 1x, 2x, 3x ; the hundredth 1c, 2c, 3c. 1 m = 1,000 c ; cm = 100,000 c ; mm = 1,000,000 c ; 12 c = 1 in 1 with 24 cyphers after it. I give below the effects of dilution as regards polarity and relative intensity. N = neutral, that is the preparation causes a reflex which is unaffected by the magnet. + indicates the reflex is diminished or abolished by the positive pole, − indicates that the negative pole diminishes the reflex.

Experiment shows that the higher dilution, generally speaking, causes a higher intensity, that is to say there is a higher potential energy in a cm than in a 6c or 30c.

The effect of dilution varies in different substances ; this I need not go into here. We are only concerned with the general principle that dilution does alter the stored energy of the substance. Clinically all who have used dilutions know well that the effect of a low dilution and a high one are very different.

Strength of potency	Relative intensity	Polarity
3x	344	—
3c	3,666	—
6c	4,333	—
12c	31,111	N
30c	42,222	N
1m	62,222	N
cm	73,333	N
mm	84,444	N

Solids varied in intensity and polarity. The above are the average intensities of about thirty common drugs.

I suggest that the increase of energy is due to the spreading out of the atom. In each dilution and shape the electrons are wider spread than in the last, and therefore they have to travel faster ; pace means energy.

Some chemists have found matter in dilutions up to the 30th centesimal ; above this it is suggested that there is no atom, merely electrons. Electrons are said to be all the same whatever substance they come from.

Against this is the fact that the highest dilution yet made, an mm, still retains all the frequencies present in the original substance. Those of the atomic number, the atomic weight, and the frequencies due to the original electrons are all present.

If no single atom is present this is strange. Personally I doubt if any chemical test is delicate enough to recognise a single atom of a substance, or any really small number.

If sulphur atoms be not present in an mm then a very potent " ghost " is present.

It is possible that in these high dilutions we have matter in a rather different plane. Something akin to the etheric. If we have no matter as known to chemists we have matter which can act on protoplasm for good or evil. This matter, which gives a far greater intensity or activity than a solid, may be definitely on a plane above the ordinary physical plane. Something akin to the auric frequencies which cannot be perceived by the normal eye.

What we do know is that it is vibrating at a higher rate than a solid and is clinically more active.

In the chapter on Colours I show that higher ohmage means a shorter wave-length. At present I must leave the question only very partially solved, but the evidence as far as it goes is clear, there is biophysical evidence of a greater energy in a high dilution than in a low one.

The homœopath selects his remedy and the particular potency by experience ; those who use a testing circuit select the dilution which best corrects errors in balance. They match frequency in drug to frequency in body and match corresponding intensities.

For example in a *B. morgan* infection I find a high intensity for sulphur, for which I give a mm of sulphur. If the liver be the principal site of infection the liver activity is lowered and I give probably carduus marianus 6c to correct this and assist in excreting the *B. morgan* and its toxins, a 6c preparation being somewhat above the normal intensity of body frequencies.

These combined potencies must meet approximately the whole picture of lost balance if they are to correct it.

The nearer we can get to estimating the total loss of balance the more successful we shall be in correcting it.

The orthodox Hahnemanian would give a single drug ; for this he has good reasons, as it is by no means easy to combine drugs, but when one can test it it is easier and there are, as I have measured in diseased conditions, not only exaggerated intensities but lowered ones.

The powerful blow of a high potency will assist Nature towards balancing things, but the repeated small taps of a low potency are also useful in establishing a more rapid balance.

II

Table I gives relationship between organisms and drugs. Table II for convenience reverses the relationship. Table III gives a relationship between tissues and drugs. They are of course incomplete, but I have made a beginning and they are based on the fact of having frequencies in common. I find them of use in daily work. I find that by using eliminators I can get rid of the toxins produced by the use of high potencies far quicker than if I use high potencies alone. The list of organisms and drugs can be very largely increased later, but I cannot include a drug unless I can prove it by my method.

Table III gives the highest intensity frequencies of drugs.

Table IV of organisms and nosodes ; the latter are made from diseased tissues.

DRUG TABLE I.

Organism or vaccine	Concomitant drugs
Lueticum and Syphilinum	Arg. nit., ars. alb., baryta carb., bismuth, calc. ars., calc. carb., card. mar., cedron, chimaphila, china, conium, eupatorium, euphorbia, euphrasia, hydrastis, iodine, kalmia, ledum, mercury, nat. mur., phytolacca, plumbum, pot. iod., pulsatilla, quinine, sanicula, sepia, silica, solidago, staphisagria, tarantula
Malarian	Ars. alb., baryta carb., cedron, china, nat. mur., pulsatilla, quinine, sanicula
Tuberculins	
Bacillinum	Nux vom., sulphur
Koch	Ant. tart., ars. alb., belladonna, bismuth, cactus, cicuta, croton, crotalus, lilium tigrum, lycopodium, nux vom.
Denys	Belladonna, bismuth, bovista, cactus, cicuta, crotalus, iodine, lilium tigrum, lycopodium, mentha pulegium, nux vom., pulsatilla
Marmorek	Nux vom., pulsatilla
Avian	Calc. carb., murex, rhus tox.
Bovinum	Carbo animalis, sulphur
Koch residue	Rhus tox.
Frog tubercle	Lilium tigrum, nux vom.
Fish tubercle	Crotalus, fucus, pulsatilla
Streptococci	Sulphur
S. anterior poliomyelitis	Cannabis indica, ailanthus, ignatia, phosphorus, sulphur, thlaspi
S. cardioarthritiditis	Aloes, eupatorium, glonoin, formica, phosphorus, podophyllin, secale, sulphur
S. erysipelitas	Ars. alb., graphites, neodynium, sulphur
S. faecalis	Ledum, nux mosch., murex, phosphorus, spigelia, sulphur
S. haemolyticus	Mercury, nux mosch., sulphur
S. mucosa	Sulphur, hepar sulph.
S. mutans	Calc. carb., mezereum, nux mosch., podophyllin
S. mastoiditis	Sulphur
S. non-haemolyticus	Neodynium, nux mosch., sulphur
S. rheumaticus	Anacardium, lilium tigrum, sulphur, xanthoxyl
S. scarlet fever	Mercury, sulphur
S. viridans	Cannabis indica, cedron, cupressus, eupatorium
Staphylococci	
S. aureus	Cactus, hepar sulph., mentha pulegium, pulsatilla, ruta, stannum
S. pyogenes	Hepar sulph., stannum, manganese
S. cereus	Cactus, pulsatilla, rhus tox., stannum, manganese
S. salivarius	Hepar sulph., mentha, pulegium, ruta

DRUG TABLE I—*continued.*

Organism or vaccine	Concomitant drugs
B. coli	.. Berberis, cantharides, cannabis indica, colchicum, collinsonia, colocynth, cupressus, dirca, cactus, euphorbia, euphrasia, formica, ferri phos., glonoin, helonias, ignatia, iodine, ledum, nux mosch, hypericum, podophyllin, tarantula
B. paracoli	Formica, iodine
B. bachii	.. Actea racemosa, ammon. carb., cactus, caladium, croton, cratægus, digitalis, origanum, ornithagalum, platinum, silica, spigelia, spongia tosta, strophanthus, staphisagria
B. Gaertner	Actea racemosa, argent nit., chelidonium, cicuta, cactus, chenopodium, mentha pulegium, nat. mur., platinum, sabina, staphisagria
B. proteus	Argent nit., card. mar., calc. ars., gelsem., mercury cor., nat. mur., strontium bromide, cocculus
B. Morgan	Ars. alb., bismuth, card. mar., carbo veg., conium, croton, glonoin, hypericum, hydrastis, lapis alba, rhus tox, solidago, sulphur, strophanthus, lycopodium
B. Flexner	Ars. alb., cantharides, colchicum, hellebor., ipecac., spigelia
Dysentery, type non-lactose	Ipecac., spigelia, sulphur
Bach's muco bacteria ..	Ruta, secale
Psittacosis	Ammon. crab.
B. welchii	Cactus, carbo veg., borax, aluminium, calc. sulph., strophanthus
Cholera	Ammon. carb.
B. typhosus coli ..	Anacardium, baptisia, bryonia, chimaphila, chlorine, gelsem., nux vom., rhus tox.
B. paratyphosus A ..	Ancardium, chimaphila, thlaspi
B. paratyphosus B ..	Anacardium, berberis, helonias, murex, podophyllin, thlaspi
B. paratyphosus C ..	Anacardium, helonias, thlaspi
B. fæcalis alkaligenes ..	Actea racemosa, petroleum, phosphorus, plumbum, tarantula
B. mutabilis ..	Aloes socot., plumbum
Monilia psilosis (sprue) ..	Graphites
Bach's polyvalent ..	Hydrastis
NEISSERIAN GROUP.	
Gonococcus	Thuja
Peterson's neisserian	Cyclamen, thuja
Medorrhinum	Calc. carb., thuja
CATARRHAL GROUP.	
Micrococcus catarrhalis	Ant. tart., cactus, calc. carb., cyclamen, nux vom., sabadilla, thuja
Corynebacterium coryzæ	Ant. tart., sabadilla
B. influenzæ	Ars. alb., ant. tart., croton, cinnamon

DRUG TABLE I—*continued.*

Organism or vaccine	Concomitant drugs
B. bronchisepticus	Actea, ant. tart., belladonna, calc. carb., petroleum, phosphorus
B. pertussis (whooping-cough)	Belladonna, drosera, rumex
Pneumococcus, type 1	Bryonia
Pneumococcus, type 2	
Pneumococcus Friedländer	Sulphur, bryonia, belladonna
Diplococcus of measles	Ferri phos.

VARIOUS ORGANISMS.

Klebs-Löffler	
Diphtheria	Aconite, belladonna, crotalus
Erysipelas suis	Graphites, solidago
Melandrinum (grease in horses)	Silica
Anthrax	Apis mel.
Tetanus	Mezereum, silica
Tetanomorphus	Gelsemium
Lyssin (hydrophobia)	Carbo veg., silica
Meningococcus	Argent. nit., belladonna, calc. carb., cicuta, echinacea
B. pestis Parel (plague)	Ferrum
Glanderinum	Calc. carb.
Parotidinum (mumps)	Phos. acid.
Sclerosinum (sclerosed tissues)	Silica
Malta fever	Calc. sulph.
B. tumefaciens	Formica, primula, pulsatilla
B. neoformans	Sulphur
Ringworm	Graphites, picric acid, sulphur
Trichophyton tonsurans	
Trichophyton sulphuricum	Graphites, sulphur
B. Koch-Weeks	Euphorbia, euphrasia, rhus tox.
B. Morax-Axenfeld	Sepia, sulphur, euphrasia
B. brucella abortus	Mentha pulegium, murex, xanthoxyl
B. ammoniagenes	Hepar sulph., cactus, sulphur
B. botulinus	Carbo veg., nat. mur.
B. acidophilus odontolyticus	
B. leprosy	Belladonna
B. paratuberculinum	Nux vom., pulsatilla

DRUG TABLE II.

Drug	Vaccines
Actea racemosa	B. Gaertner, B. bachii, B. fæcalis alkaligenes, B. bronchisepticus
Aconite	Diphtheria
Ailanthus	S. anterior poliomyelitis, B. coli
Aloes	B. mutabilis
Aluminium	Welchii
Ant. tart.	Koch, micrococcus catarrhalis, B. influenzæ, bronchisepticus

DRUG TABLE II—*continued.*

Drug	Vaccines
Anacardium	S. rheumaticus, B. typhosis coli, bronchisepticus, micrococcus cartarrh., paratyphoid A, B, C
Apis mel.	Anthrax
Argent nit.	Meningococcus, B. proteus, B. Gaertner, cancer, syphilis
Ars. alb.	B. influenzæ, malarian, Morgan, syphilis, B. Flexner, Koch, S. erysipelitas
Apocynam	Cancer
Baptisia	B. typhosus coli
Belladonna	B. pertussis (whooping-cough), B. bronchisepticus, Koch, Denys, meningococcus, cancer, diphtheria
Berberis	B. coli, B. paratyphosus
Borax	B. welchii
Bovista	T. B. Denys
Bryonia	Pneumococcus types 1 and 2, B. typhosus coli
Baryta carb.	Syphilis, cancer coli
Bismuth	Morgan, Denys, Koch, syphilis
Cactus	B. coli, welchii, micrococcus catarrhalis, staph., cereus, Gaertner, bachii, Denys, Koch
Caladium	B. bachii
Calc. ars.	B. proteus, syphilis, cancer
Calc. iod.	Cancer
Calc. sulph.	Cancer, welchii, Malta fever
Calc. carb.	T.B., avian, S. mutans, glanders, micrococcus catarrhalis, syphilis, bronchisepticus, medorrhinum, meningococcus
Cannabis indica	S. viridans, B. coli, S. ant. poliomyelitis
Cantharides	B. Flexner, B. coli
Card. mar.	B. proteus, B. Morgan, cancer, syphilis
Carbo. veg.	Welchii, lyssin (hydrophobia), Morgan
Carbo. animalis	Bovinum
Cedron	S. viridans, malaria
Chenopodium	B. Gaertner
Chelidonium	Gaertner, cancer
Chimaphila	B. paratyphosus A, cancer, syphilis
Chlorine	B. typhosus coli
China	Malaria
Cicuta	Meningococcus, Gaertner, Denys, Koch
Cinnamon	B. influenzæ, cancer
Cocculus	B. proteus
Colchicum	B. Flexner, B. coli
Colocynth	B. coli
Collinsonia	B. coli
Cratægus	B. bachii
Croton	B. bachii, Koch, Morgan, B. influenzæ
Crotalus	Fish tubercle, diphtheria Koch, Denys
Cyclamen	Micrococcus catarrhalis, Peterson (Neisserium coccus)
Cupressus	B. coli
Conium	Cancer, syphilis, Morgan

Drug Table II—*continued*.

Drug	Vaccines
Dirca	B. coli
Drosera	B. pertussis (whooping cough)
Digitalis	Bachii
Echinacea	Meningococcus
Euphorbia	B. Koch-Weeks, syph., B. coli
Euphrasia	B. coli, Koch-Weeks, syph.
Eupatorium	S. cardio-arthritidites, syph.
Ferrum	B. pestis
Ferri phos.	Diplococcus of measles, B. coli
Formica	B. coli, cardio-arthritidites, B. paracoli, tumefaciens
Fucus	Fish tubercle
Fuligo	Cancer
Gelsem.	B. proteus, typhosus, cancer, tetanomorphus
Graphites	Sprue, S. erysipelas, erisipelas suis, ringworm
Glonoin	B. coli, Morgan, S. cardio .
Hepar sulph.	Staph. pyogenes, S. salivarius
Helonias	B. paratyphosus, B. coli
Hellebor.	B. Flexner
Hydrastis	Bach's polyvalent, cancer, Morgan, syph.
Hypericum	B. Morgan, B. coli
Ignatia	S. anterior poliomyelitis
Iodine	Denys, B. coli, syph.
Ipecac.	B. Flexner, dysentery type (non-lactose)
Kalmia	Syphilinum
Lapis alba	Morgan, cancer
Ledum	Syphilinum, B. coli, S. fæcalis
Lilium tigrum	Denys, Koch and frog tubercle, S. rheumaticus, cancer
Lobelia erinata	Cancer
Lobelia inflata	Cancer
Lycopodium	Koch, Denys, B. Morgan
Mentha pulegium	Cancer, Gaertner, Denys, Staph. aureus and salivarius
Mercury (metal)	Syphilis, S. hæmolyticus, S. scarlet fever
Mercury cor.	B. proteus, cancer
Mezereum	Tetanus, S. mutans
Murex	Cancer, S. fæcalis, avian T.B., B. paratyphosus B
Neodynium	S. erysipelitas, S. non-hæmolyticus
Nat. mur	Cancer, B. proteus, Gaertner, malaria
Nux mosch.	S. fæcalis, S. non-hæmolyticus, S. mutans, B. coli
Origanum or Ornithogalum	Cancer, B. bachii
Petroleum	Fæcalis alkaligenes, B. bronchisepticus
Picric acid	Ringworm
Platinum	Cancer, Gaertner, bachii
Plumbum	Cancer, syphilis, B. mutabilis, fæcalis alkaligenes
Phos. acid.	Parotidinum (mumps)

DRUG TABLE II—*continued*.

Drug			Vaccines
Phosphorus	..	..	S. ant. poliomyelitis, S. fæcalis, B. bronchisepticus, S. cardioarthritiditis
Podophyllin	..	..	Cancer, S. cardioarthritiditis, S. mutans, B. coli, paratyphoid B
Pot. iod.	..	..	Syphilis
Pulsatilla	..	..	Tuberculins, Koch, Denys, Marmorek and Fish, Staph. cereus, syphilis
Quinine ..	..	..	Malaria
Rhus tox.	..	..	Morgan, typhosus, S. cereus, avain T.B., Koch-Weeks, Koch residue
Rumex ..	..	..	Pertussis
Ruta	..	..	Cancer, Bach's muco-bacteria, Staph. salivarius
Sabadilla	..	..	Mic. catarrhalis, C. coryzæ
Sabina	..	..	Gaertner
Sanicula ..	..	..	Malaria, coccal co.
Secale (ergot)	..	..	S. cardioarth., Bach's mucobacteria
Sepia	..	..	B. Gaertner, Morax-Axenfeld, syph., cancer
Silica	..	..	Syphilis, cancer, sclerosinum (thickened tissue), tetanus, malandrinum, bachii
Spigelia ..	..	..	S. fæcalis, B. Flexner, B. bachii
Spongia tosta	..	..	B. bachii
Staphisagria	..	..	Cancer, syphilis, Gaertner, bachii
Strontium bromide	..	..	B. proteus
Strophanthus	..	..	Morgan, welchii, bachii
Solidago ..	..	..	Syphilis, cancer, Morgan
Symphytum	..	..	Cancer (any bone disease)
Sulphur ..	..	..	Cancer, Morgan, streptococci, dysentery, bovinum, bacillinum
Thuja	..	..	Gonococcus, medorrhinum, Peterson, catarrhalis
Thlaspi ..	..	..	Ant. poliomyelitis, paratyphoids
Tarantula	..	..	Fæcalis alkaligenes, coli, syphilis
Xanthoxyl	..	..	S. rheumaticus, cancer

Locality of tissue		Drugs
Nervous system ..	..	Phosphorus, argent. nit., indium, cicuta, calc. carb., nat. mur., hypericum, hyoscyamus, staphisagria
Pineal gland	..	Indium
Thyroid	..	Iodine
Parathyroid	..	Calc. carb.
Breast ..	..	Belladonna, conium, chimaphila, phytolacca, scophularia nodosa
Lymphatic glands	..	Scophularia nodosa
Stomach	..	Ornithagalum, cactus, carbo veg., condurango, staphisagria, nux vom.
Duodenum	..	Ornithagalum, belladonna
Small intestine ..	..	Lobelia inflata, lobelia erinata, anacardia, sulphur, belladonna, nux vom., card. mar, ferri phos., æsculus
Colon	..	Lobelia inflata, lobelia erinata, sulphur, card. mar., hydrastis, solidago, ruta

DRUG TABLE II—*continued.*

Locality of tissue	Drugs
Pancreas	Berberis, iris, æsculus, capsicum, ornithagalum, card. mar.
Liver	Card. mar., sulphur, hydrastis, solidago, anacardium, capsicum, crocus, cuprum, lycopodium, berberis
Rectum	Ruta, hamamelis, hura braziliensis, scrophularia
Kidney	Lycopodium, solidago, hydrastis, berberis, formica
Gall-bladder	Berberis, thlaspi, helonias
Urinary bladder	Berberis, formica, petroleum, staphisagria, cantharides
Mucous membrane	Sedum acre, hydrastis
Lung	Belladonna, rumex, ferri phos.
Spleen	Æsculus, ferri phos., hydrastis, pennyroyal
Bone	Arnica, symphytum, formica, kidney extract, bone-marrow, eupatorium, hypericum
Sex system	Pennyroyal, murex, dirca, staphisagria, ignatia, nux vom., caladium, thlaspi, helonias, origanum, xanthoxyllum
Skin	Sulphur, tin, manganese, arsenic

I have left out the method of stimulating an organ by a potency made from itself ; this is best done at 6 c. as a rule. The above drugs I use in 6 c. strength in nine cases out of ten, in the exceptions I use the mother tinctures. For treating kidney-stones or a condition tending thereto I have used calculus 6 c. ; for gall-stones cholesterin 6 c.

TABLE III.

HIGHEST INTENSIVE FREQUENCIES OF DRUGS.

Abrotanum	63,883	Ammon. chlor.		74,005
Absinthum	73,913	Anacardium..		86,912
Aconite	35,171	Antimony, crude		12,177
Actæa racemosa	63,163	Anagallis		60,804
Adonis vernalis	81,314	Antimony, tart.		39,151
Adrenalin	10,998	Antipyrene		23,561
Æsculus	93,290	Apis mellifica		11,522
Agaricus	49,313	Apocynum		44,118
Agrimonia	71,236	Aqua marina..		80,031
Agnus Castis	32,620	Aralia		31,125
Ailanthus	96,336	Aranea diadema		42,633
Allium cepa ..	61,942	Argent. nit. ..		18,614
Allium sativa	80,509	Arnica		81,252
Aloes socotrina	58,012	Arsenicum album		62,620
Alstonia	27,243	Artemisia		62,352
Aluminium	36,154	Asafœtida		13,230
Alfalfa	45,340	Aspirin		61,801
Ambra grisea	14,815	Aurum		28,436
Ammon. carb.	81,160	Animosa		28,113

150 THE CHAIN OF LIFE

TABLE III—*continued.*

Arvensis	.. ..	17,245	Chenopodium	..	90,146
Argyrol	.. ..	25,736	Chimaphilla	..	77,706
Agarol	.. ..	72,290	China	.. ..	61,134
			Chorallium	.. ..	33,600
Baptisia	.. ..	75,169	Chrysophanic acid		98,141
Baryta carb.	..	31,311	Chrysarobin	..	22,410
Belladonna	..	76,290	Cicuta	.. ..	53,115
Bellis	..	23,904	Cina	.. .. ..	52,800
Benzoic acid	..	98,031	Cinnamon	..	16,151
Berberis	..	47,653	Clematis	.. ..	55,415
Bismuth	..	96,190	Cobaltum	..	21,717
Borax	..	36,022	Coccus cacti	..	74,412
Bovista	..	46,224	Coccalis	.. ..	96,302
Bryonia alba	....	63,441	Coffea	.. ..	60,316
Bufo ..	..	57,813	Colchicum	..	66,124
Borneol acetate	..	19,616	Collinsonia	..	79,327
Bidor ..	.. ..	11,430	Colycynthis	..	72,921
Boron	.. ..	28,591	Condurango	..	71,814
Barium	.. ..	23,700	Convallaria	..	32,961
Beryllium	..	30,072	Conium	..	59,412
Bromum	.. ..	37,114	Cratægus	..	51,522
			Cocaine	..	21,428
Cactus	..	43,151	Crocus	.. ..	46,224
Cadmium sulphas	..	81,711	Crotalus	..	73,006
Cæsium	..	60,999	Croton	.. ..	37,251
Caladium	..	72,954	Cupressis	..	88,421
Calamine	..	88,289	Cuprum	..	65,226
Calc. ars.	..	74,410	Cyclamen	..	12,490
Calc. carb.	..	22,427	Chicor indicus	..	80,442
Calc. phos.	..	61,813	Corycine	..	54,660
Calc. fluor.	..	78,154	Cotyledon	..	62,456
Calc. lactate	..	72,927	Caprokol	..	14,627
Calc. sulph.	..	60,462	Camomile	..	62,590
Calc. iod.	..	12,271	Contramine	..	43,311
Calendula	..	48,071	Cerato will.	..	90,051
Calotropis	..	40,179	Chloretone	..	41,035
Camphor	..	31,714			
Cannabis indica	..	38,503	Daphne	..	42,627
Cantharides	..	71,854	Digitalis	.. ..	55,150
Capsicum	..	97,025	Dioscorea	..	88,363
Carbo veg.	..	13,119	Dirca	.. ..	83,704
Carbo animalis	..	51,913	Drosera	..	81,714
Carbolic acid	..	15,550	Dulcamara	..	34,904
Carbon	..	15,034	Dielectric oil	..	41,552
Carduus marianus		85,315	Dextrose	..	83,917
Cascara sagrada	..	25,573			
Caulophyllum	..	81,626	Echinacea	..	62,180
Causticum	..	54,141	Elaps ..	..	30,623
Ceanothus	..	61,584	Elaterium	..	40,281
Cedron	..	72,625	Ephedrine	..	94,404
Cepa ..	..	34,230	Epiphegus	..	22,431
Cereus bonplandii	..	49,420	Eupatorium	..	98,010
Cerium	..	69,341	Euphorbium	..	23,150
Chamomilla	..	31,601	Euphrasia	..	63,012
Chelidon	..	45,321	Equisetum	..	11,725

TABLE III—*continued.*

Erbium	51,590	
Egg Shell	23,740	
Egg-white	71,802	
Egg membrane ..	14,321	
Ferrum metallicum ..	75,521	
Ferrum phos. ..	62,910	
Ferrum oxide ..	15,968	
Filix mas	62,874	
Fluoric acid	69,119	
Formica rufa.. ..	24,054	
Fucus	37,140	
Fuligo ligni	71,675	
Galium	27,591	
Gelsemium	26,571	
Gentian lutea ..	47,732	
Glonoine	70,044	
Graphites ..	87,411	
Gratiola	45,282	
Guaiacum	93,630	
Hamamelis	80,643	
Hæmostatic serum ..	40,121	
Helleborus niger ..	85,512	
Helonias	71,720	
Hepar sulph. ..	25,289	
Heroin	40,576	
Hura braziliensis ..	24,352	
Hydrangea	78,731	
Hydrastis canadensis	16,085	
Hyoscyamus.. ..	71,220	
Hyoscin	57,051	
Hypericum	53,562	
Hydrochloric acid ..	22,318	
Hydrocyanic acid ..	70,744	
Hydrocotyl ..	20,240	
Ignatia	31,914	
Impatiens roylei ..	64,520	
Indium	88,061	
Ilon abscess salve ..	33,812	
Insulin	34,180	
Infludo	35,741	
Iodine	93,610	
Intramine	53,322	
Ipecacuanha.. ..	71,912	
Iridium	51,514	
Iris versicolor ..	74,118	
Jaborandi	75,300	
Jacaranda caroba ..	59,502	
Juglans regia ..	49,123	
Kali bichromate ..	72,114	

Kali bromatum ..	81,801	
Kali carbonicum ..	61,132	
Kali muriaticum ..	46,421	
Kali phosphoricum ..	75,211	
Kali sulphuricum ..	44,460	
Kalmia	31,241	
Kreosotum	58,311	
Lac. caninum ..	34,624	
Lachesis	83,116	
Lapis albus	82,410	
Latrodectus mactans	45,644	
Lactuca virosa ..	49,058	
Laurocerasus.. ..	39,440	
Lithium	70,228	
Ledum	88,106	
Lilium tigrinum ..	71,550	
Limulus	41,466	
Lobelia erinata ..	25,361	
Lobelia inflata ..	87,321	
Lolium	38,243	
Lycopersicum ..	62,952	
Lycopodium	42,411	
Lycopus	42,130	
Lysamachia	51,040	
Magnesia muriatica..	86,021	
Magnesia phos. ..	78,653	
Magnesia sulph. ..	58,807	
Manganese butyrate	14,510	
Manganum ..	89,442	
Marshmallow ..	84,503	
Medinal	41,624	
Mentha pulegium ..	33,356	
Mephitis	48,005	
Mercurius met. ..	95,512	
Mercurius cor. ..	22,421	
Mercury cyanatus ..	23,454	
Mezereum	85,530	
Millefolium	48,274	
Molybdinum ..	48,724	
Mimulus	37,451	
Moschus	97,100	
Murex	27,380	
Mygale	31,550	
Naja	81,620	
Naphthaline ..	60,890	
Natrum mur. ..	45,139	
Natrum phos. ..	83,362	
Natrum sulph. ..	13,380	
Nitric acid	72,113	
Nux mosch.	51,151	
Nux vomica ..	28,311	

TABLE III—*continued.*

Œnanthe	.. ..	23,300	Salicylic acid	..	13,805
Oleum cajuput	..	73,381	Salvarsan ..	..	38,521
Opium	.. ..	56,831	Sambucus ..	..	69,326
Origanum	..	51,625	Sanguinaria ..	..	61,355
Ornithagalum		53,603	Sanicula	..	51,531
Osmic acid	..	91,291	Santonin	.. ..	
Oxalic acid	..	64,200	Sarsaparilla ..	..	61,324
Oxygen	.. ..	61,002	Scleranthus	..	47,391
			Scrophularia nodosa		88,060
Palladium	.. ..	40,413	Secale cornutum	..	67,450
Passiflora	.. ..	60,340	Sedum acre ..	..	24,348
Pelletierene ..	..	50,319	Selenium	..	86,321
Pepsin	.. ..	50,914	Sempervivum	..	54,903
Peptone	.. ..	83,744	Sepia	.. ..	12,717
Petroleum	.. ..	60,308	Silica	.. ..	79,131
Phaseolis	..	38,226	Sodium	.. ..	46,051
Phosphoric acid	..	40,021	Soda cacodylate	..	38,080
Phosphorus ..	..	43,560	Solidago	..	38,760
Physostigma		38,010	Sparteine sulph.	..	52,455
Phytolacca	..	65,403	Spigelia	..	20,277
Picric acid	..	81,721	Spongia tosta	..	31,460
Pilocarpus	..	75,300	Stannum	.. ..	21,160
Piper mephisticum	..	48,119	Staphysagria	..	44,080
Piper nigrum		38,550	Sticta pulmonaria	..	44,560
Platinum	..	13,419	Stramonium	..	18,312
Plumbum	..	20,720	Strontium brom.	..	58,614
Plantago major	..	22,244	Strophanthus	..	54,400
Podophyllum	..	81,812	Sulphur	.. ..	60,901
Polygonatum	..	28,238	Sumbal	.. ..	72,024
Polonium	..	97,711	Symphytum	..	71,301
Primula obconica	..	41,734	S.U.M. (36)	..	14,142
Pulex irritans	..	57,414	S.U.P. (468) ..	..	32,854
Pulsatilla	.. ..	11,916			
Pyrites	.. ..	85,041	Tabacum	.. ..	31,212
Prickly pear leaf	..	31,501	Tantalum	.. ..	10,415
Ditto, large	..	81,141	Taraxacum	..	80,871
Ditto, small	..	82,141	Tarantula hispania	..	88,088
			Tellurium	..	61,624
Quinine	..	55,710	Terebinthum	..	44,512
Quinine salicylate	..	42,327	Teucrium scorodonia		72,234
			Thallium	..	38,887
Radiostol	..	32,460	Theelin	..	14,422
Radium	..	22,595	Thlaspi	..	14,392
Radium bromide	..	96,208	Thorium	..	27,211
Rheum	..	41,003	Thuja	..	43,119
Rhodium	..	17,818	Thiohistamine	..	28,351
Rhododendron	..	27,781	Thiosinaminin	..	62,527
Rhus tox.	..	53,073	Trinitro toluene	..	85,502
Rosemary	..	90,346			
Rumex crispus	..	91,251	Uranium	..	57,221
Ruta ..	..	74,454	Urtica urens ..	..	44,086
Sabadilla	..	86,241			
Sabina	..	52,518	Valerian	..	58,811
Sabal serrulata	..	60,902	Valibrom	..	22,702

TABLE III—*continued*.

Vanadium	..	72,350	Xanthium spinosum	61,424
Veratrum album	..	68,320	Xanthoxylum ..	43,114
Veratrum viride	..	19,721		
Verbascum	..	37,155	Yttrium	95,005
Verbena ..	..	43,802	Ytterbium	16,323
Viburnum ..		36,405	Zinc sulph. ..	41,848
Viola odorata	..	73,141	Zingiber	90,334
Viscum album	..	33,200	Zirconium	33,121

TABLE IV.

HIGHEST INTENSIVE FREQUENCIES ORGANISMS.		B. proteus	33,499
		B. dysentery (Flexner)	78,340
Gonococci	34,688	B. dysentery (Bach.)	78,788
Neisserian catarrhalis		B. coli communis ..	98,591
(Petersen)	12,490	B. bachii	38,231
Micrococcus crassus	21,334	B. mucobacteria (Bach.)	32,530
Micrococcus catarrhalis	15,886	B. psittacosis ..	81,578
Micrococcus melitensis	14,604	Vibrio choleræ ..	33,807
Corynebacterium cory-		B. typhosus ..	41,988
zæ hofmani ..	78,989	B. typhosus in Pyer's	
Corynebacterium		patch	47,393
pseudo-tuberculosis	63,456	B. paratyphosus A ..	38,978
B. influenzæ	99,880	B. paratyphosus B ..	21,999
B. bronchisepticus ..	76,074	B. paratyphosus C ..	13,700
B. tuberculosis (Koch's		B. welchii	71,703
type)	57,732	B. fæcalis alkaligenes	98,989
B. tuberculosis (Denys		B. mirabilis	91,105
type)	74,250	B. polyvalent (Bach.)	86,103
B. tuberculosis (Mar-		B. Morax-Axenfeld ..	54,824
morek type) ..	91,840	B. pyocyaneus ..	13,750
B. tuberculosis (avian		Streptococcus mutans	57,520
type)	73,622	Streptococcus cardio	
B. tuberculosis (bovine		arthritiditis ..	82,502
type)	82,916	Streptococcus viridans	92,240
B. tuberculosis (fish		Streptococcus erysi-	
type)	27,540	pelatis	21,741
B. tuberculosis (frog		Streptococcus scarlet	
type)	61,675	fever	30,414
B. tuberculosis (Koch's		Streptococcus anterior	
residue)	84,483	poliomyelitis ..·	83,416
Cancer virus (from Rous		Streptococcus non-	
sarcoma)	80,441	hæmolyticus ..	67,188
Leishmani donovani		Streptococcus hæmo-	
(kala-azar) ..	94,002	lyticus	77,610
		Streptococcus fæcalis	26,677
		Streptococcus rheu-	
INTESTINAL ORGANISMS.		maticus	65,071
		Streptococcus mastoid-	
B. Morgan	97,979	itis	66,024
B. Morgan-Gaertner	50,660	Streptococcus mucosus	83,390
B. Morgan-Patterson	34,114	Streptococcus infre-	
B. Gaertner	45,664	quens	81,295

TABLE IV—*continued*.

Streptococcus havens. group	46,174	B. acidophilus (type I)	53,472
Staphylococcus aureus	48,889	B.acidophilus (type II)	53,160
Staphylococcus pyogenes (17)	30,032	B. acne (Ponsonby)	47,134
Staphylococcus cereus flavus	60,200	Amœba dysentery	15,850
Staphylococcus salivarius	36,254	Vibrio paracholeræ	22,955

Staphylococcus albus (86)	17,340	**NOSODES.**	
Staphlococcus pyogenes albus (63)	41,291	Carcinosin	53,160
Pneumococcus (types1)	35,301	Carcinomin	31,760
Pneumococcus (types2)	52,310	Cancro. pan.	60,042
Pneumococcus mucosa (Dixon)	32,471	Epitheliomin	13,425
Pneumococcus Friedländer	22,440	Schirrhinum	70,330
Meningococcus	16,021	Malandrinum	31,715
Diplococcus (measles)	74,272	Anthracene	30,030
Trichophyton tonsurans	31,820	Lyssin (hydrophobia)	40,254
Trichophyton sulphurans	36,262	Sycosis co.	32,455
C. diphtheriæ (Klebs-Löffler)	65,004	Lueticum	72,323
B. erysipelatis suis	62,206	Syphilinum	88,037
B. tetani (Tulloch)	41,124	Medorrhinum	77,130
B. tetanomorphus	57,530	Psorinum	81,640
B. pertussis	70,261	Sclerosinum	41,649
Monilia psilosis	37,652	Parotididum	47,405
Monilia albicans	50,940	Variolinum	56,014
B. pestis	38,276	Epihysterinum	24,582
B. lepræ	90,244	Bacillinum (T.B. and Strep.)	90,261
B. tumefaciens	15,707	Calculus	32,504
B. botulinus	41,314	Pyrogenium	41,419
B. ammoniagenes	24,410	Vaccinum	24,272
Brucella abortus	53,442	Variolinum	56,014
B. neoformans	36,250		
B. Koch-Weeks	28,318	**BODY COMPOUNDS.**	
		Urea	60·05
		Guanidine	59·06
		Cholesterine	58,201
		Calcium oxalate	43,782
		Uric acid	16,807
		Ethyl alcohol	46,050

Numbers in brackets refer to Lister Institute Catalogue.

CHAPTER XVII

THE NATURE OF CANCER

I.

IN undoubted cases of cancer I find the following changes have taken place :—

(1) There is present the virus found by Gye and Purdy recognised on the altered reaction on the frequency 80,441. If the living virus be present there is a positive reaction on both sides of the abdomen which repeat on two rheostats.

(2) Guanidin is present in the blood in excess.

(3) Urea is deficient.

(4) At the site of the growth even when it can hardly be detected with the fingers there are found gland frequencies above normal for some of the internal secretory glands, especially sex and parathyroid.

(5) Deficiency of these same glands to a corresponding extent.

(6) Atoms mostly show an increased charge on nucleus and deficiency of electrons.

(7) Increase of hydrogen electrons.

(8) Certain frequencies show an increased positive charge.

(9) Changes in B. biomorphs which is diagnostic of cancer and sarcoma.

I will deal with each of these diagnostic points in order, but first I will say a few words as to the controversy as to whether cancer is a local or general disease. We are all agreed that cancer is the result of long-continued irritation ; this may be caused by tar or soot locally, or by the use of charcoal stoves as in the Kanga district in India where the inhabitants warm their tummies with a small charcoal heater ; betel nut is also thought to cause cancer ; smoking short clay pipes supplies an irritant in other cases. Tubercle, chronic intestinal toxæmia, syphilis or other bacterial infection, especially *B. gaertner*, are other predisposing causes.

Whatever the cause may be it has to act over a considerable

period. Now it is impossible to have long-continued irritation even very locally without general changes taking place.

The above changes show a general change in the body. Macdonagh and Koch of U.S.A. have described blood changes. Koch regards cancer as a protective effort to form a gland, largely parathyroid. Macdonagh calls cancer Nature's last ditch of defence and advises the use of ageratin, a substance made from sex glands. They both describe local and general changes.

I do not see how anyone can seriously maintain that general changes do not take place in cancer ; you have only to look at patients who have had a growth for any time to see they are thoroughly toxic.

I should describe cancer as a local response to a general condition.

The cancer virus is localised in a way that is not usual with bacterial disease. In an early stage it is easy to miss when testing. To this extent cancer is local, but the general condition of toxæmia has existed long before, the cancer stage was reached. Not one of the above changes is local except the presence of the living virus and this is preceded by the cells producing a corresponding toxin. None of these changes takes place in the early stages of disease ; they are the result of a long-continued process.

Cancer can be diagnosed from a drop of blood. This will show guanidin in excess, but it may not show the virus unless a special technique is used, and the virus reaction can be missed unless this is used.

I will now discuss these changes in the order given above.

II.—THE VIRUS.

For a long time many people have had the idea that cancer was due to an organism of some sort. Before I went out to India I attended a medical smoking concert and heard a topical song entitled " The Man who found the Spores in Carcinoma," sung to the tune of " The Man who broke the Bank at Monte Carlo." In those days the idea of a living virus was something of a jest. Gye and Barnard's work brought this idea nearer reality. The monumental work on cancer by Drs. Gye and Purdy will, judging by the reviews of the book, change the views of the profession. If sarcoma can be produced in fowls by a virus it must be produced in animals and man by a virus. Those who wish to study Gye and Purdy's evidence will read their book. Very shortly, what they did is this : They treated material from a Rous chicken sarcoma by heat and other means till all chicken cells and ordinary bacteria were killed and the only thing left alive was an unfilterable virus. This could be kept in a dried state for considerable periods, and when injected into the breast of a fowl would reproduce the sarcoma locally. This settles the matter as far as fowls are concerned. Technical difficulties have hitherto prevented them from obtaining the same virus from human growths.

Working with my circuit I can obtain evidence which it is difficult to obtain in any other way. Dr. Gye has very kindly supplied me with some of his material which is alive and active. This gives a highest intensity wave on 80,441 ohms which repeats. This wave occurs in altered polarity in all the sections of sarcomas and carcinomas which I have examined—twenty-five at the time of writing. These are all from human beings, and further it is present in cases of carcinoma which give all the other signals which I have found present in carcinoma. Some of these are obvious—to the eye, in carcinoma of the breast and epithelioma in the mouth. Most of the other cases have palpable tumours or thickening of the breast or internal organs.

Carcinoma in a moderately severe case gives the reaction 80,441 74+ +, i.e. a positive reaction on both sides of the abdomen. This wave can be tuned to by using either figures on the rheostats in the primary circuit or using the vaccine in the secondary circuit. In this case, however, the correct dose only will give a reading of 74 in the secondary circuit. This method is a check on the figure reading.

To my mind there is no doubt that the virus causing cancer or accompanying it is practically the same thing that causes the Rous chicken sarcoma.

(1) The highest intensity wave, 80,441, is present in human cases.

(2) A vaccine made from the material acts favourably on cancer cases and reduces 80,441 to normal reactions provided other suitable treatment is given. I will deal with this under treatment.

(3) This 80,441 frequency occurs over the growth in altered polarity and balance and repeats on 2 rheostats, giving the sign of a living virus.

(4) When 80,441 occurs in altered balance as a single non-repeatable frequency it indicates the presence of a toxin only, not the organism. This takes place along lines of lymphatics, glands, and along certain nerve tracks. For instance, if the

ovaries or uterus are affected, the sex centre in the brain gives 80,441 = 74 neutral, a cell change.

I have also found it present in an unbalanced condition on certain spots on the palm of the hand. These spots, I am told by Mr. Jaquin, who has made a scientific study of the hand, were connected with the organs affected. This was checked up in various ways to eliminate mental action. There is no doubt that toxins from the growth affect the nervous system, but growths do not spread along these nerve lines. They follow lymphatic connections.

III.

The presence of guanidin molecular weight 59·06 = 74+ + when the virus is present. When the toxin only is present guanidin gives a neutral reaction. When 95.06 guanidin gives a 74+ + reaction, urea gives a 74— —. If guanidin = 40 neutral, so does urea. I have never found this guanidin excess in any other condition than carcinoma or sarcoma. The excess of guanidin is closely allied to para-thyroid action in many cases but not in all.

IV.—CHANGE IN ENDOCRINE GLANDS IN CANCER.

I give below a table showing the readings for the principal endocrine glands in six cases, contrasting the condition of supply in the growth and in the blood. These have been confirmed in a number of cases in sections from growths and blood taken from cases. It will be seen that in all the recorded cases, where a gland supply was found low in the general blood-stream, it was high over the growth. They happened to be all female cases, and the very low reactions for the ovarian hormone in the blood are most striking. Parathyroid and cerebral hormones are almost as low. All these three are invariably high over the growth. The parathyroid, as I have shown, has a special connection with both testes and ovaries.

	Case I		Case II		Case III		Case IV		Case V		Case VI	
	B.	Gro.	B.	Gro.	B.	Gro.	B.	Gro.	B.	Gro.	B.	Gro.
Ovary	3	74	3	71	3	72	2	71	2	71	4	71
Parathyroids	2	74	4	68	3	70	2	73	7	72	7	72
Thyroid	6	70	23	73	20	51	12	52	4	70	14	70
Cortex	11	70	17	71	49	24	3	61	4	46	8	46
Medulla	47	8	50	25	18	52	50	15	34	38	43	38
Pineal	7	63	11	44	5	70	4	60	5	70	4	70
Thymus	3	72	4	70	5	70	1	62	4	71	6	71
Ant. pituit.	20	51	41	21	12	63	34	41	35	39	37	39
Post pituit.	32	41	36	38	34	39	42	40	39	41	39	41
Cerebral	2	74	1	74	4	71	4	70	5	71	5	71

This kind of gland action is not peculiar to cancer. The same kind of thing takes place round a tubercular nodule ; in this case parathyroid is very high round the tubercular focus and low in the blood-stream. Doubtless it is a general phenomenon in a healing effort but most marked in cancer.

I think the figures in the table do suggest that Koch is correct in saying that there is an attempt to form a gland. It might be more correct to say that the available hormones go to the spot where there is the greatest need for their action. Do we not get a hint here as to the cause of the intense proliferation of cells at the site ?

The sex glands are connected with cell multiplication, their frequencies cause new cell formation. The constant stimulus by sex hormones must cause cell proliferation. Ovaries and testes are very rich in samarium and illinium, the 62nd and 61st elements. These elements are found in high intensity in all the growing points in plants—ends of roots, terminal shoots, points of leaves. They are closely connected with active cell growth.

This point has a very important bearing on treatment. If you level up on sex gland you not only buck up some patients generally but you lower the activity of an important factor in proliferation of cells. In fact you very materially check abnormal cell divisions.

I suggest that possibly the following is the sequence of events. We can for the moment drop the question of whether Gye's virus is the original irritator.

(1) The process starts as an inflammatory stage due to irritation—tar or other.

(2) The weakened cells call for help, the endocrines supply protective substances, this call is operated by the law of electrical attraction and repulsion.

(3) The endocrines send the needed supply.

(4) The cells become over-stimulated and keep on dividing.

(5) They give an over-supply of positive electricity. They have large nuclei which are positive and comparatively small cell bodies which are negative (cf. Prof. George Crile's views).

(6) This over-supply of positive electricity is communicated to other neighbouring cells. These form big nuclei as a consequence.

(7) Cells escape and start the process elsewhere.

Cancer occurs in those who are prematurely old with poor sex secretion and a low supply of endocrine hormones generally.

(8) As I have shown elsewhere this gland action is not confined to cancer, it occurs in other conditions to smaller

extent.   The above tables were taken from late cases; in earlier cases only one or two glands show excess over the growth.

V.—ALTERED POLARITIES IN CANCER.

This next point in cancer formation is less easy. to understand.   Gland secretion, yes, that is easy to understand ; changes in the atom, that is another matter.

Though the intelligent layman will read about the atom, about astronomy, the big atoms of the cosmos, many doctors have told me that talk about the atom was beyond them. This is really mental laziness.   After a bit they listened and got the idea quite clearly.

The following table is a chart of what happened in a cancer growth and in the second stage of pneumonia.   Normally, in the atom, the charge of electricity on the sun or nucleus is equal to the charge on all its electrons put together.   This keeps it in electrical equilibrium.   In health this condition is maintained as a whole, though life necessitates change, yet healthy life means change within certain limits.   Every time you think you cause changes in the atoms.   In disease the physiological limit is exceeded, and instead of healthy change, swing and counter-swing, we find a tendency to stasis in one position.   Either the charge on the nucleus is too great or the charge on the negative portion of the atom is too great.

In the cosmos there are forces driving atoms—suns, satellites —towards a certain centre or swinging them out to the periphery.   What goes on outside our bodies goes on inside them. In cancer the forces drawing electrons to the centre exceed the dispersive force.   In inflammatory disease the dispersive force is in the ascendant.

This may seem to be a matter beyond our ken and not practical, but it is a matter of the very greatest importance and of very practical use, as I shall now show.

This dispersion and concentration of electrons corresponds to Macdonagh's blood particle phenomenon.   What is true in one case is true in another.   Macdonagh tells us that anything which causes dispersion of blood particles tends to cure cancer.   He quotes erysipelas and certain other infections.   These forces of concentration to a centre and expansion outwards are most important in the cosmos.   When our earth was formed it contracted from particles drawn out from the sun, the astronomers tell us.   They also tell us that the cosmos as they know is constantly expanding.   The life-

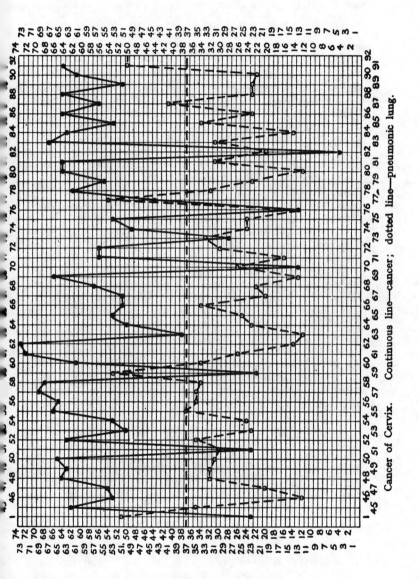

Cancer of Cervix.   Continuous line—cancer;   dotted line—pneumonic lung.

forces with us expand and contract as shown by the changes in our aura.

This ebb and flow is part of the history of nations—expansions and then local concentrations and the formations of new nations. Dispersion and concentration, contraction and expansion are, perhaps, as important factors as the positive or male and the negative or female elements in the cosmos.

I have already related, in the chapter on Inflammatory Disease, the action of the elements 13 to 17 in regard to dispersion, and that they act with greatest effect at 6-c strength. This is probably the reason why one finds that the Gye virus vaccine acts best at 6-c in the early stages, but it is well to add one of the above elements as well. I discover which by test. If we consider cancer from a microscopic point of view the cancer virus is closed in by a mass of cells in a way which does not ordinarily occur in inflammatory disease. It is therefore necessary to use something to loosen the surrounding mass and secure elimination of the virus. This has to be done slowly ; too much toxin must not be set free at a time.

Another viewpoint of cancer is obtained of the cancer growth by examination with the galvanometer. When one electrode is placed on the forehead on the same spot as the subject is connected in my circuit and another electrode placed over the growth, the movement of the light on the galvanometer screen is very small, sometimes nil. In inflammatory conditions movement is rapid. This indicates that the growth is dense and resistant to the natural body currents. A. E. Baines discovered this and used salt solution for treating growths. This also points to the need for using dispersers. If salt is used to get the chlorine action, 6-c is the strength indicated.

To cause expansion of the electrons from the centre of the nucleus of the atom we must use one of the following : aluminium, silica, phosphorus, sulphur or chlorine, or some drug containing these. They will also act on the growth itself and merely by ionising with common salt I have seen a patient lose all his toxic symptoms, put on flesh and become free from pain.

Looking at the growth from a morphological point of view it is obvious that we need to soften it. From the electronic point of view we need to rectify balances and from the bio-physiological view we need to loosen up the densely packed tissue to allow toxins to be liberated. The obvious things to use are the above elements, which are dispersers.

VI.—ALTERED FREQUENCIES IN CANCER.

In inflammatory disease there is an increase of the lævo-rotatory or negative compounds ; in cancer the dextro compounds are increased.

The following reactions when they are found + + are indicative of active cancer with a live virus. They are taken from a variety of cancer vaccines in my possession. I give the concomitant drug which goes with each in a number of cases when they are used for treatment.

Vaccine	Tuning	Concomitant drug
Carcinosin	31,760	Solidago, hydrastis
Carcinomin	53,160	Calendula
Carcinomatin	82,118	Helonias
Epitheliomin	13,425	Sedum acre. Fuligo ligni (soot)
Schirinum	70,330	Aloes. Silica
Cancro-pan	60,042	Apocynum. Picric acid

34,502 is a frequency common to 20 specimens I possess, and seems regularly found present in cancer. 74,635 is a frequency which is fairly common and is given by potato-eye, a remedy I used with success in some cases up to a certain point.

VII.—CHANGE IN BIOMORPHS.

Carcinoma and sarcoma cause, or are accompanied by, changes in the B group of biomorphs. The tuning of this group in the five layers is 3/ï/7/2/9/ from without inwards. This group of biomorphs is always affected in malignant disease and not in any other condition in my experience so far. A lowered reading for this group is therefore diagnostic.

The outer layer of 33 tuning, what I term the human layer, is always contracted ; in place of extending over several feet it may contract so that it extends for only two or three feet. Every layer may be affected, the width of the band in the aura diminished and the activity tuning lowered. Usually I find that in addition to this outer layer only the three inner layers are affected, the third or reptilian layer, i.e. 777, is most markedly affected. If the 111 layer is involved the case is very severe.

In very slight cases the vegetable layer only may be affected, but this is unusual. In one case of sarcoma I asked two clairvoyants to examine him. They saw the patient within a few days of each other. Both reported that only three layers of the aura were affected ; in his case the three inner layers showed loss of intensity but the 111 layer was clear.

The 333 layer must have been diminished as this occurs in all cases of illness, but apparently this diminution is not visible. These gentlemen, Mr. Thomas and Mr. Buckingham, also reported all the spots affected by sarcoma which I found, and both of them also noted a faint cloud on the right side of the chest.   This was a spot where an injection of arsenic had been given a year before.   This, they said, only affected one layer. This corresponded with my findings.   This spot was very faintly sarcomatous.

This method of inspection seems to have a considerable advantage, as a clairvoyant can get an immediate view of the whole body and can spot lesions one might miss.   Mr. Thomas's view was taken while I was in another room.   Both inspections were made without a word from me as to where lesions were situated.   Mr. Thomas also stated that he felt the original trouble had started at the back of the throat and had caused pressure in the ear.   It seems he had this sensation himself.   This was going into past history as the patient's acute symptoms had started in the pharynx and had caused inflammation of the Eustachian tubes and immense pressure on the ear which had to be pierced.   Any explanation of this going into the past is beyond me, but the sensation of the present is a common experience of my subject.   These sensations are probably due to biomorphic vibration.

The fact that cancer affects a different group of biomorphs which are never apparently affected in any other condition points to the condition being essentially different from any other disease.   The C group are also affected, but not A and B. These, as far as the four-layer biomorphs are concerned, remain apparently unaffected, the 33 tuning which is common to all the four biomorphs is affected in all disease.

VIII.—Lighthouse Effects.

Further, there is in cancer what I have described as the " lighthouse effect."   When you examine elements by themselves you get the effect I described in the chapter.   In inflammatory conditions this is absent.   A swing may occur in hyperthyroid cases.   In every cancer case so far examined it is present.   There is a definite swing backwards and forwards from positive and negative.   The positive reaction is present for so many seconds, then it disappears and the negative phase begins, but this is shorter than the positive. This effect was discovered by Mr. Dudley D'A. Wright, F.R.C.S., when he was working with me.   The phenomena are by no means simple and vary on different wave-lengths.

Since then Dr. Wright and I made a number of experiments to try and produce the phenomena with inflammatory conditions under test, by introducing various drugs not needed by the patient, but we were unable to get the phenomenon. At any rate my results are regular. I get this phenomenon only in cases which present the series of reactions typical of cancer and sarcoma and hyperthyroidism. It has not occurred spasmodically as it should do if this were due to contamination.

There is a different effect, what I should term a latent period, which is caused by introducing a drug into the circuit which affects the reactions. Here a temporary disturbance is caused but the reactions settle down again. Also, if too high a potency is used, there is a swing-over to the other side. This is permanent if the drug is left in the circuit, but while the drug is being moved a swing-over is caused. This may be the effect noticed by Boyd and others.

I agree with Dr. Boyd that if reactions are not obtained something is wrong with the apparatus, but there is a certain latent period for all reactions. If you try the on and off test there is always some delay in reporting the signal. This is due to the time that the waves take to travel along the wires and nerves, and it will probably vary with different observers and possibly different subjects.

IX.—When does Cancer Begin ?

I consider that cancer begins when I find the cancer virus present. Before this I should call the condition pre-cancerous. The surgeon requires a palpable lump, but by the time this happens the cancer is well advanced and the cancer toxins are already in other organs.

One does not require a certain area of membrane to decide a case is diphtheria ; the presence of the organism and signs of its local and general action are sufficient. The virus is not present till certain cell-changes have taken place. Glands enlarge in the neighbourhood of a growth before the virus spreads to them.

X.

We have therefore in cancer a local response to a general condition, almost certainly at first an attempt at cure. Koch reports that he had seen patients whose general health improved after the cancer growth started. Ultimately, if not dealt with, the cancer cell becomes, as Macdonagh says, parasitic to the host. Cancer is connected with the growth of the Gye-Purdy virus, but there are other growths which are connected with *B. morgan.*

In all the sections I have of adenomas, fibro-adenomas and uterine fibroids I have obtained a reaction for *B. morgan.* This class of growth gives a reaction 52,414 ohms. Morgan bacilli also give this reaction, though it is not their highest intensity wave of personal rate. If I add *B. morgan* to a normal blood it causes the 52,414 ohms frequency to give an unbalanced reaction.

The connection is suggestive. Morgan causes boils and does a number of other things, but the connection with fibroma is too frequent to be accidental. It has always been present in the uterus with uterine fibroids. In fatty tumours the reaction 93,560 = 74 is found, which is the highest intensity wave in glanderinum, a preparation from glanders. It may be the case that each kind of growth is a local response to the action of organisms.

A further point in favour of the connection between uterine fibroids and *B. morgan* is that lapis alba, which is a well-recognised remedy for fibroids, is also a concomitant drug for Morgan and has a frequency in common. In fact Morgan gives off the H.I.F. for lapis alba.

Very few phenomena in nature are singular. If cancer is the response to the Gye-Purdy virus, other tumours will almost certainly be the response to other invaders. Or, conceivably, we may find that Morgan grows well in a fibroid, the cancer virus in a cancer growth.

All the evidence I have goes to point to the view that soil changes come first and that flora follow. When a specific flora is developed it may act as an irritant causing further changes.

To recapitulate cancer is a local response to a general condition, with a local excess of gland hormones in which the virus grows, with changes in the auric frequencies of a kind present in no other condition.

It affects at long last every atom in the body and every layer of the aura. It is the last stage of disease.

ANALYSIS OF THE ROUS CHICKEN SARCOMA.

After Treatment by Drs. Gye and Purdy's Process to Extract the Virus.

Reactions were taken on atomic weight figures. Figures used were taken from Hodgman and Lange, 1928 ed. Figures in brackets were worked out by myself to nearest fraction possible and checked on atomic numbers. Intensity figures are given in actual ohmage. Elements which gave slight reactions are omitted.

Element	At. wht.	Intensity	Element	At. wht.	Intensity
Hydrogen ..	1·008	51,111	Indium ..	114·9	22,222
Carbon ..	12	25,555	Tin ..	118·7	32,222
Sodium ..	23	64,444	Tellurium ..	127·5	24,444
Phosphorus ..	31·03	35,555	Iodine ..	126·93	28,888
Sulphur ..	32·06	64,444	Cœsium ..	132·81	14,444
Chlorine ..	35·57	72,222	Lanthunum ..	138·90	42,222
Potassium ..	39·10	72,222	Cerium ..	140·25	23,333
Calcium ..	40·07	53,333	Praseodynium	140·9	51,111
Vanadium ..	50·96	13,333	Neodynium ..	144·27	31,111
Manganese ..	54·93	24,444	Illinium ..	(148·20)	72,222
Iron	55·84	34,444	Samarium ..	150·43	72,222
Copper ..	63·57	13,333	Holmium ..	165·4	31,111
Zinc	65·38	13,333	Rhenium ..	(187·3)	12,222
Arsenic ..	74·96	32,222	Gold ..	197·2	31,111
Yttrium ..	88·9	12,222	Mercury ..	200·6	43,333
Zirconium ..	91·00	14,444	Lead ..	207·20	31,111
Molybdenum	96·00	21,111	Radium ..	225·95	42,222
Palladium ..	106·7	11,111	Thorium ..	232·15	14,444
Cadmium ..	112·41	33,333	Uranium ..	238·17	22,222

Note that the six most important elements are sodium, sulphur, chlorine, potassium, illinium and samarium. The sex glands supply the two latter. Sulphur is usually the best diffusion agent. Chlorine has been most useful in the form of ionisation with common salt, the negative pole over the growth. Potassium has been used as a remedy in Cantassium. But it is important to use the right compound and potency as the following table shows. The cancer virus was placed in the dynamiser. Its intensity measure = 88,888. Drugs in form of 6-c were then introduced in turn. The resulting intensities are noted below. Those noted with a cypher were less than 1 ohm.

Hydrastis ..	..	0	Ornithogalum	..	211
Card. mar. ..	..	0	Penny royal ..	..	211
Pot. bich. ..	..	0	Guiacum ..	..	211
Scroph. nodosus	..	0	Aloes ..	..	211
Tin ..	..	0	Solidago ..	..	211
Podophyllin ..		0	Fuligo ..	..	88,888
Phosphorus ..		0	Potato eye ..	..	22,222
Chlorine ..	..	0	Lobelia erinata	..	61,111
Sulphur ..	...	0	Lobelia inflata	..	61,111
Cadmium sul. ..		0	Silica ..	..	32,222
Ars. alb. ..	..	11	Gentian ..	..	71,111
Calc. ars. ..	..	111	Pot. sulph. ..	..	111,111
Symphytum ..		11	Nat. mur. ..	..	111,111
Ruta	..	11	Platinum ..	..	111,111

XI.—TREATMENT OF CANCER.

Before discussing the medical treatment of cancer I must
say a few words in regard to operation. Believing, as I do,
that cancer is of curable condition, I am naturally averse
to operation unless for mechanical reasons, such as blocking
of the bowel, contraction of the stomach or some condition,
apart from the actual disease, which threatens life.

The position, however, to my mind, is not so entirely simple
as many followers of Abrams or some homœopaths appear
to consider. It is entirely untrue to say that operation
always fails. I have not been in a position to follow up many
of my operation cases, they disappeared in India, but of the
few cases operated on in England one lady whose breast I
removed with the pectoralis major and axillary glands was well
and fit five years later with no sign of recurrence. This was not
an early case either. The growth had been present for at least
five months when I saw it, and probably had been present a
good deal longer. This lady was also given superficial ray
treatment before and after operation.

I have never seen permanent benefit from crippling operations. In any case general treatment is always needed,
but where a breast can be removed I think there is a case for
discussion.

The surgeon will urge that the operation is soon over and
that the dangerous virus is removed with it. The physician
can treat the case afterwards and in any case medical treatment
must take some time and in the meantime the patient is
exposed to great risk.

To this I should reply that medical treatment with a vaccine
should be carried out first and the danger of spreading the
infection was less after such treatment than before. My
great objection to immediate operation before the virus
has been tackled is that the shock of operation and opening
up of tissues lays the patient open to a fresh infection. The
virus having been killed one has to choose between operation
and removal of the tumour and dealing with this by medical
means.

If time can be given for treatment and the patient can
come to me regularly, I should advise against operation.
I have seen breast growths disappear under treatment and I
think that scar tissue is a great disadvantage. I am rather
inclined to agree with Koch that the remains of a growth
can be a benefit to a patient provided it is not an inconvenience
mechanically.

To prevent recurrence we must treat the patient at regular intervals to change the soil so that she is no longer in danger. This must be done anyhow, operation or no operation, if the general condition is to be corrected.

In cases which can be operated on without crippling the patient the surgeon may well raise the question as to whether the cancer cell, apart from the virus, is not a danger, and whether ultimate treatment is not assisted by removal of the growth. He may say : " Granted that you have means of treating cancer successfully in some cases, would there not be less risk to the patient's life to remove the particular spot of suitable soil which may form a site for a return of active growths ? Seeing the difficulty there is in securing immunity, is it wise to handicap yourself by leaving something which must take a very long time to tackle ? Will the patient's strength be sufficient to remove the growth ? Does she not run greater risks by prolonged stimulation than she would by an operation ? "

These are questions which must be faced without prejudice. We have to balance up the disadvantages of either course. On the one hand there have been numerous cases where cure has taken place—a number of cases have been published by homœopaths in this country, and there have been some wonderful results by Abrams' followers, both here and in America. I have myself had a number of cases which got well and remained well, and also failures. But this discovery of Gye and Purdy's makes our chances far better than they were before. Still, there is no doubt that whatever course you take there are risks. A number of cases have gone wrong because too big a stimulus was given, or the patient's vital powers failed. True, in these cases, there was nothing to show the cancer virus had been killed. In a year of two I shall be able to be much more definite pro or con.

There is another group of cases in which I am inclined to agree to operation : an easily removable tumour of an abnormal kind which in itself is a nuisance, say a superficial fatty tumour or a polypoid fibroid. There seems to be very little point in keeping such tumours. Once they have become malignant they may as well be removed, for you have here a difficulty in getting normal cells to invade them. I would deal with the virus before operation. Such tumours I should feel inclined to operate on, however innocent they were. This is my present opinion ; I may change it later on. You can say if you like that this is inconsistent—if you do not advise operation on cancer why operate on an innocent tumour ?

My argument is this. I know I can affect cancer growths, though I have failed at long last in some old people. A fatty tumour no doubt can be affected by drugs ; homœopathic colleagues tell me they have done this, but is it worth the time and money ? Such growths shell out easily and an operation while they are innocent is no very great matter.

An operation on a bad malignant case is a very different matter. Sometimes one gets a blaze up of toxæmia shown by irritating rashes. Further, cancer has very frequently spread far beyond the reach of operation and the operation shock hastens the spread of the virus and the death of the patient.

Once the virus has been scotched the question certainly arises : Should the growth itself be removed, if get-at-able, and no serious crippling be likely to result ? We need more light on this point. The balance of my mind is rather towards leaving things alone except for an occasional gland or drug stimulant. The patient is most likely to settle this point himself, but all the same it is one's duty to form an opinion and advise for and against operation. However, before operation is performed one must be certain no virus remains undealt with.

It is conceivable that, as Koch suggests, the remains of the tumour, originally an effort at protection, are of some service. On the other hand a tumour is a foreign body and may be a nuisance mechanically, and we must always remember that the cancer cell, apart from the virus, may be a danger.

Although some very wonderful things have happened by the use of drugs alone or oscilloclast alone and more regularly good results may be obtained in the future by the use of vaccines, drugs and especially by gland products, I think the time has not come yet to be dogmatic. All the factors must be considered and I hope to see shortly the surgeon and physician co-operating, realizing the relative advantages of each other's work. I say this as one who has done a fair amount of surgery. If a growth has to be removed it can be removed more easily and safely after medical treatment than before. This question can only be ultimately settled by figures showing the results of leaving the growth to be treated by the physician and removing it. Such figures can only be true guides when absolutely comparable cases are contrasted. My feeling is that cases which have not been operated on do best.

XII.—DRUG TREATMENT.

To use the Rous sarcoma with effect as a vaccine I had to find out what dilution was most suitable. I therefore had four dilutions made ; the polarity and comparative intensities of these were as follows :—

$3^c = 1,111 + \cdot + \cdot 6^c = 111,111 - \cdot -.$ $12^c = 3,111$ neutral. $30^c = 3,111$ neutral. Obviously the 6^c being a negative preparation and the most active, was the one most likely to be effective. This proved to be the case in practice. When Dr. Gye supplied me with the Rous sarcoma material he had no knowledge of the use I was going to make of it. Later he was naturally anxious that his name might not be associated with a so-called cure for cancer. I doubt if there ever can be one substance found to cure cancer as its manifestations vary so much and it is impossible to cure the variety of precedent conditions which lead up to cancer by one remedy.

To treat cancer successfully one has to bear in mind that *the growth is a response to a general condition.* It is an attempt to supply something the system needs. The virus is probably simply the flora suitable for this type of soil. The virus is at first found in this situation only. It probably is developed from some similar organism of a perfectly harmless nature. It is important to deal with the virus because once it has developed it can, if introduced elsewhere, produce the same kind of soil. This has been shown by Gye and Purdy's experiments, and further they have shown that though the virus may be present in a fowl this does not protect it from further infection. The virus produces no general immunity. What can protect ? I should say a general alteration of soil ; this can only take place gradually, as the stimuli applied over a long period with removal of the inimical factors in the environment, one of which is almost certainly soil and water. Before giving a dose of this virus vaccine I give for three days before the principal meals a combination of certain drugs worked out by tests. In giving these I have the following aims in view : (1) A certain amount of desensitising of the patient so that the shock of the vaccine may not produce too great a reaction and make the patient feel very ill. (2) Loosing up of tissues to enable the vaccine to get at the virus in this densely packed growth. (3) To increase elimination by stimulating all the organs which are out of balance. (4) To stimulate the healthy cells surrounding the part. (5) To deal with the original condition which caused the formation

of the growth.   This is a very essential part of the treatment.
(6) To counteract the concentration of electrons at the centre
of the atoms, i.e. electronic dispersal.   For dispersal and for
softening effects it is necessary to use one or more of the five
elements 13th to 17th, i.e. aluminium, silica, sulphur, phosphorus and chlorine, or compounds containing some of these
in an active state.   The last three are those which appear to
be most often needed in the first stages of treatment.· The
following drugs contain these three elements in effective
activity and are those I have used most frequently as drainage
drugs.   For breast cases conium, phytolacca ;   stomach,
ornithogalum ;   liver, carduus marianus, hydrastis, podo-
phyllin, solidago ;   colon, lobelia, erinata ;   rectum, ruta ;
uterus, murex, mentha pulegium ;   ovaries, chelidonium.
I give a general indication of situation, but the drugs, of course,
cover a wider area than this.   In addition to dealing with the
virus I make a point of treating one or two stages of disease
which preceded the formation of the growth.   One of these
is the condition resembling syphilis ;   for this I give lueticum
or syphilinum.   I must use some eliminant for this ;   it will
probably be kalmia or will be found in the above list.   Then
I am also going to deal with the basic type of disease which
produced the syphilinum condition, andfor this I shall need
an eliminant.   In a large number of cases a tubercular
infection is found and calcium carbonate is the clearance
drug or lycopodium.

At the first test I assemble in the primary circuit vaccines
or high potency drugs plus eliminants and glands till the
patient's reactions = 49,000 for general body tuning and 37 ohms
on all reactions and the $\dot{7}$ biomorph frequency is off scale.
Crotalus or naja or another snake poison is often needed for
the treatment of tubercular trouble ;   if none of these is
needed I test for belladonna, rhus tox or lilium tigrum.   If
the cancer condition does not follow T.B., but is the result of
bowel organism or streptococcus, I give appropriate remedies
for this.   Or the condition may be due to gonococci or similar
organisms and medorrhinum is one of the first drugs to be
given in combination with the cancer virus and lueticum.
Generally speaking I try to deal not only with the virus but
approximately two stages ahead of this by vaccines or other
drugs acting as vaccines, and concomitant eliminators.   I
have not usually found it necessary to give the active virus
vaccine 6-c which is wholly a negative preparation in more
than two attacks.   At the first treatment cancer virus 6 and
accompanying high potencies are given on two, three or four

evenings on successive days. If needed this attack is repeated
in a fortnight as indicated, two to six doses. In the next
stage in dealing with the live but not active toxins a 30-c
vaccine is used. High potencies are repeated as needed.
Later on the virus 12-c may be needed, in each case with
appropriate eliminators and longer intervals between doses.
It is. usually necessary to deal with *B. gaertner* when the
syphilinum and tuberculinum stages have been eradicated.

Treatment of an actual early case was as follows :—

The patient had a small growth in the left breast with
retraction of the skin, no pain. She had been under treatment on and off for some years but had felt much better
for the last six months. She had recently consulted her doctor
about this retraction of the skin of the breast which made
her suspicious. The reactions for cancer were all present
accompanied by reactions for Koch T.B. infection of suprarenals. Right suprarenal measured 2. There was a con-
spicuous bronzing of head and neck. With low suprarenals
blood-pressure should have been low ; owing to suprarenal
activity in breast it was rather above normal. First treatment : cancer virus 6, lueticum cm., lilium tigrum cm. ;
2 doses. Cinnamon 6, pulsatilla 6, silica 6 · three times a
day for fourteen days and suprarenal gr. v daily. Second
treatment : lueticum cm., one dose ; phytolacca 6, fourteen
days. Third treatment : phytolacca 6, three weeks ; sulphur
and calc. carb., four weeks. Growth disappearing, no
signs of malignancy or of tubercle.

The following list shows the relative intensity of dispersal
elements in drugs most commonly used :—

(1)	Card. mar. 6c	..	..	88,888	88,888	88,888
(2)	Ornithogalum 6c	..	..	94,444	82,222	82,222
(3)	Solidago 6c	..	..	73,333	73,333	84,444
(4)	Scrophularia nodosum 6c	..	82,222	82,222	82,222
(5)	Ruta 6c	..	..	83,333	83,333	83,333
(6)	Mentha pulegium 6c	..	94,444	24,444	62,222
(7)	Hydrastis canadensis 6c	..	12,222	43,333	43,333
(8)	Symphytum 6c	..	..	31,111	82,222	82,222
(9)	Podophyllin 6c	..	..	13,333	82,222	10,000
(10)	Sanguinaria, 6c	..	..	—	13,333	12,222
(11)	Murex 6c	..	..	43,333	—	21
(12)	Lobelia erinata 6c	..	..	1	41,111	83,333
(13)	Belladonna 6c	..	..	31,111	13,333	72,222
(14)	Yeast (solid) ..	..	..	13,333	62,222	61,111
(15)	Sepia	..	..	..	31,111	82,222	10

The selection is made by testing first the effect of the drug
on the virus and locality which it especially· affects, and then

on the patient's aura, which represents the total effect on the individual. This is the final and supreme test, for no drug is any use which does not increase the patient's vitality.

XIII.—GLAND TREATMENT.

(1) During the early period of treatment special attention is needed for the glands, for it is the glands which are largely at the bottom of the trouble. Nature is always making efforts to balance things; the growth is originally an attempt to balance gland supply. My measurements extending over some years show this is invariably the case; if we level up gland supply the necessity for the growth has gone. This is why I object to operation *per se*. The gland I give is one of those which is surplus in the growth. Sometimes sex-gland and parathyroid are needed, more often one gland alone. This is, I believe, the gland originally affected by the basic disease, frequently in recent cases the suprarenal. In such cases lycopodium 6 is usually needed, and this stimulates the suprarenals, but normality is more quickly reached if the gland itself is given. When testing, the gland is given which brings the auric vibration which is low, usually 7 in the B series, up to normal intensity. When a gland does this you will find that during the test it has raised the other glands to normal balance, 37. It acts radio actively. The reason for giving gland tissue is that the body can make endocrine material more easily from endocrines than from any other material, although it has to be broken down and built up again. I am told that a dog can be kept going in efficiency on the smallest amount of protein provided this is dog; if other animal protein is given a larger amount is needed. In the case of the sex glands levelling-up affects another factor in the cancer cells; where sex hormones are present, there is an increase of cell activity: It is part of their essential nature. They contain the elements samarium, 62nd element, and illinium, the 61st, always present in the growing points of plants in roots, leaves and stems. Levelling up these elements reduces the tendency to cell reproduction. As a rule 25 tablets of suprarenal gr. v given one daily is sufficient, or ovarian gr. v or parathyroid gr. 1/10. In a number of cases a fortnight's treatment is sufficient. In addition to giving the key gland or glands a stimulant of these glands must be given. I firmly believe in finding the simillimum for the case treatment of the patient's vitality is the primary aim, but in cancer of all conditions this is not easily achieved unless all available factors are con-

sidered and the complex condition present in cancer is not easily treated by giving one drug or one vaccine.

(2) After the virus and its toxins have been expelled, the glands levelled up, the subsequent condition must be measured up and treated. We shall now be treating a condition which I classify under inflammatory disease, but at the back of one's mind one must always have the possibility of recurrence of the cancer condition and keep a careful watch for the first sign. The patient must continue under treatment till every frequency is normalised and all signs of disease have disappeared. Even then examination should be made quarterly for a considerable period.

(3) Results on the whole have been good ; there have been, of course, a number of failures, some cases which have made a promising start. Such relapses have been due to two causes, mostly because vitality has failed, some because underlying causes have not been dealt with sufficiently quickly at the start ; sometimes advice has not been followed, sometimes the importance of the underlying cause was not sufficiently realised ; in some of the bowel cases mechanical obstruction has occurred. Apart from cases probably doomed from the start there has been in a few cases prolonged delay over recovery owing to outside causes, unhealthy surroundings ; one or two cases have cleared up after moving to another house or another district ; unhappy home conditions ; over-work ; business worries ; continued infection from husband or other member of the family. The psychological side I have dealt with in a separate section.

(4) Prognosis is not easy to make. Two of my cases which made the most rapid recovery were women over 60. Both had rectal cancer, both were diagnosed by an experienced practitioner as cancer, both gave all the signs which I have enumerated, both were clear of all signs of malignancy inside two months, and growth had disappeared. Among a number of youngish people treated the removal of the cancer toxins was prolonged and fluctuated with a tendency to return to activity at intervals. In two cases of cancer of the cervix when I originally saw them the cervix was hard, thickened and fixed, and the reactions were as usual. After the cervix had become freely movable and normal to touch in every way a discharge still remained. In one case this was due to gonococcus and in another to streptococci. In both the cancer toxin remained = 40 neutral. Gonococcal infections in women are notoriously hard to remove. I have had a number of cases where this organism was found in the vagina,

two in virgins, which was the last sign of the activating condition which produced cancer. The presence of gonococci does not mean necessarily venereal disease. I have found it in a large number of cases who certainly had not acquired it that way. The gonococcus only produces its typical results where it has been passed on from person to person and has acquired a certain virulence. It can be grown in suitable soil from a milder form of organism. In the two cases mentioned above the husband also had a similar infection ; in neither were there signs of venereal trouble, but a general infection in which the prostate played only a part. The usual treatment adopted by homœopaths, medorrhinium and thuja, was only partially successful. Lac caninum M.M. is more effectual in delayed cases with sodium sulph. 6 as a drainage remedy. In all cases every possible angle of the patient's life must be considered and attended to as far as possible. I have had cases which came to me for purely mental symptoms where I found malignant growths. The mental symptoms cleared up after physical balance had been established. The removal of toxins gives time for the mind to recover itself. Strains in mental life cause changes in body chemistry. What acts one way can act in another. Drugs can cause disturbances on the emotional and mental planes and also can act with benefit.

I also use colour and the oscilloclast in the treatment of cancer as well as in other conditions. Their use is described in chapters on those remedies. The use of colour is most important and quite definite rules can be given for use of colour in cancer. Once this condition has started everyone appears to be alike as regards colour, that the series of colours used are the same. The key to the treatment of cancer is to realise it is a biological process, not a weird entity coming from a source entirely outside our control. The early stage is a definitely favourable one for the treatment of the whole person, for their vital resources are making a definite effort at health. Such remedies are used as will raise the auric frequencies to normal activity, though remedies are thought out on definite lines no remedy is given unless it increases the life-forces of the patient.

XIV.—Psychological Treatment of Cancer.

There are two marked psychological features in cancer : fear and sex strain ; one or both has been present in all my cases. Fear may be due to the presence of the virus or its toxin, but I think it is fear which produces the soil suitable for the growth of the virus, and my experience has been that cases do best when facts have been faced. There is an initial shock, but when this is got over everything is easier. Measuring by frequencies does not tell us anything about lumps or form of organs whatever they may suggest. A patient may have guanidin present in excess and the active virus present and not have what a surgeon would call cancer clinically, although these are always present in every malignant growth, but there is always some thickening to be felt when the organ affected can be examined with the finger. This must be kept in mind when talking to the patient. When the patient is ready to talk about his fears or sex history it is best for him to make a clean breast of things. It is a relief to talk out to someone else things that have been either secretly encouraged or repressed.

I have a great belief in drainage physically and mentally ; at the same time one can assist to relieve strain with drugs. Cadmium sulphas, arsenic, or one of the Gaertner concomitants for fear, and one of the sex-centre drugs for the sex difficulties, such as caladium, dirca or staphisagria.

In these fear cases pineal is often useful, for the cancer patient has a contracted aura and is apt to be egocentric.

The psychological treatment is very important and needs to be varied for each individual just as much as the drug treatment. No hard and fast lines can be laid down, one has to feel one's way and find out the strong and weak points in each character.

The most important thing is to restore morale.

XV.—RESULTS AND SUMMARY.

Between January, 1932, and June, 1934, I have treated a little over one hundred persons in whom I found the cancer virus active. It will take some time to analyse these. It is only by recording results of consecutive cases that one judges of the merits of any line of treatment. So far I know that seven of these have died. There may be deaths among those I have lost sight of, but these are not likely to be many as the majority did not cease treatment until advised that no further treatment was needed. A considerable number of these cases would not have been recognised as cancer without a blood test. All of them gave the signs which I have described in the early part of the chapter. In every case where digital examination could detect a change a tumour or thickening was felt.

Allowing for the fact that a large number were diagnosed early the results are extremely encouraging.

Of the seven deaths four were very advanced cases undertaken to give relief. One died from influenza just after the loss of a beloved husband. She was clear of all signs of malignancy.

I do not wish to encourage the idea that results comparable with these can be obtained with cases at the usual stage at which they are recognised, but I do wish to emphasise two points, (1) that cancer can be recognised early, and (2) that it is by no means an incurable condition. Some of the cases treated were at first very unfavourable ; they were elderly women with a very long history of bad health and well-marked signs of tumour and hæmorrhage.

I have sometimes found that women beyond the active sex age were easier to clear of signs of malignancy than younger ones in whom there was some sex strain. There is a lot more work to be done in regard to treatment and in obviating masking which sometimes occurs at the first test, but a beginning has been made. I trust in future others will use the tests I have discovered and that increasing use will be made of the Bendien test.

Success in dealing with cancer depends on recognising that there is a virus, an altered balance in gland secretion and that there are always other infections and all three conditions must be dealt with. Any method of combating cancer which ignores this is seriously handicapped from the start.

CHAPTER XVIII

DIETING

DISEASE is a matter of soil. An extremely important factor in determining the kind of soil is the food we eat. The flora of our intestines is very largely decided by what we put into them. The majority of people nowadays do not overeat, but the kind of food taken is very often badly selected. Many volumes have been written on dieting, but I have always found a difficulty in dieting patients until I worked out a system on my circuit. Since I have tested this method I have had no difficulty. I test out the effect of food-stuffs on the lowest frequency in the aura. I only permit the foods which markedly stimulate the biomorphs. In some cases I check up on uric acid, or a cancer or asthma frequency. The result is the same as regards forbidden foods, or if these increase uric acid they lower vital action.

It is futile to give vaccines or drugs and at the same time to allow the patient to reproduce the conditions which you are trying to alter. If your patient has a streptococcal infection, potatoes and rice form an excellent soil for its growth.

Individuals vary so much that food selection is as much a special treatment as drugs. The same argument for using a mechanical aid in the choice of drugs applies to food. Every human being is different. How can any system of dieting detect that lemons will agree but grapefruit will not ? Or that milk and cream are good, but not butter. Some patients, by long experience, have learnt what suits them and mainly what does not. They are not seldom mistaken, by reason of tastes. The majority have not given much thought to the matter except to avoid things which constantly disagree. One vast advantage of testing is that one avoids fads.

ALCOHOL.

Probably there is no article of diet about which so much has been written as alcohol, or such strong language used. A great deal of money is invested in the production of alcohol, and it is the business of the trade to represent it as almost necessary to life. On the other hand because individuals have abused it we have in the United States the spectacle of prohibition and all it connotes, and we have in the British Isles a series of Acts intended to diminish the sale of alcohol.

In judging whether alcohol is good for my patients I depend solely on the reflexes on my subject's abdomen ; this reflex has no opinions, prejudices or fads ; it is automatic, you might say mathematical. When testing for alcohol " yes " or " no," I do not care a cuss which way the answer goes, but again, though one often says " No alcohol " the answer is by no means always quite so emphatic. The various forms are tested. Sometimes one can say " A little whisky but nothing else," or it may be stout or cyder. Work on wave-lengths and not on theories. The world might be better as a whole without alcohol in view of man's weakness, but this does not alter the fact that Mrs. Brown would be better for a little stout at the time of testing, or that a glass of port would be helpful to Mr. Smith.

Far more often than not I have to say " No alcohol at all." I used to take my whisky peg regularly in India, but I refused short drinks as a personal habit, though a tot at the right time was immensely comforting. I always maintained it was imbecile to drink stuff you did not want, out of politeness ; that good fellowship which required cocktails was not worth having. At the same time, though I have no great use for alcohol personally, except as an occasional fillip or *bonne bouche*, I am ready to go out gunning if anyone wants to prevent my having my quarterly tot.

Alcohol can be a food and a valuable one at certain times. In some cases it stimulates the digestion and gives the whole man just the fillip he needs. In other and more frequent cases it is the very last thing a sick man wants. I took over a military hospital once, full of pneumonia cases. The young doctor in subordinate charge to me believed in alcohol. There had been deaths ; all the pneumonias were on alcohol, their hearts were getting blocked. After going over each case carefully I cut off all the alcohol and gave most of them an injection of morphia. I cut down food to fluids. My subaltern prophesied numerous deaths, but the whole lot were much better next day and all recovered.

There is no drug which has been more abused than alcohol, but when we need it nothing else can take its place.

An acute attack of crampy pain in the abdomen may be promptly relieved by hot whisky or brandy.

A major in my regiment, an expert on diet, too much so

poor chap, cured me of a nasty feverish catarrhal condition with one brew. " The Mess President will now undertake the doctor's case," he said. Feeling perfectly miserable I consented, and swallowed a most delectable jorum of port, brandy, cloves and other flavourings available in the mess stores. I went to bed quite happy and jolly, the blankets, were piled on and I woke next morning free of catarrh after a fine sweat. This may have been a lucky shot, but many years before that I cut short an attack of 'flu by a tremendous go of champagne plus hard dancing. In those days, however, the biomorphs must have been very active fellows.

As one gets older one eliminates alcohol less easily, and if one wants to work one cannot afford to use foodstuffs that are harmful or merely neutral merely because they are pleasant.

A doctor is apt to get one-sided views because he only deals with the sick. Is alcohol any use to young people doing hard work? I cannot say for certain. I have not measured up a sufficient number. Personally, I always cut it out when training for running and got very fit without it, but Rugby and rowing men seem to do quite well on beer. The Cambridge school of experimental psychology has shown that alcohol slows up mental reflexes, but I think that the dose of alcohol they gave was excessive. For boxing and sprinting, where everything depends on a quick reflex, I should advise avoiding alcohol.

The very few experiments I have made on healthy young people make me inclined to believe that they are better without alcohol altogether, especially if they want to be sharp off the mark.

VEGETARIANISM.

The prohibition of meat is another fad, especially among Theosophists. What does our reflex method say about this? The reply is generally that some meat is wanted, the reflex cares not a bit about the patient's views, but it is rather striking how often the reflex has agreed about meat with the views of the patient. At the same time a number of Theosophists and other vegetarians for conscience's sake need meat, and some of them have found by experience that they cannot do creative work without it. They have then, like sensible folk, realised that they are here to work, and the perfect life from a dietetic point of view was not for them, however much they might have liked to adopt it.

It may be preferable not to live on our little brothers, but our ancestors have done so for geological periods, and habits

are not easily changed. To give up meat unless it benefits
you to do so is foolish ; if we all gave it up to-morrow we
should have to slaughter a large proportion of our herds. It
is alleged that meat is bad for cancer cases ; that is true in
about only 50 per cent., the others are better for having
meat. At one time I was inclined to believe what food faddists
and persons claiming occult vision told me about cancer.
I treated all cancer cases without meat, but I soon found that
this was wrong, and remember well how one case bucked up
when meat was restored to his dietary.

Human nature mentally always desires to lay down laws
and find out routine remedies. Unfortunately physical
human nature refuses to act up to these rules. There are
always a certain number of iniquitous exceptions which are
better for beef and even beer. I have yet to find the cancer
case who is better on alcohol, but it will turn up some day if
I see a sufficient number.[1] There is a tale going round that
tomatoes are bad for cancer. It is so in the majority of cases,
but it is not universal.

One would like to be able to work out rules for diet for this
and that condition, and what would be helpful to others
not working on the same lines, but my work makes me an
individualist.

There are some rules I do believe in and advise :—

(1) Use fresh food. English for choice, because it is
    fresher.
(2) Quick cooking does less harm to vitamin content
    than prolonged.
(3) Avoid re-cooking things.
(4) Eat meats dry if possible, but don't make yourself
    uncomfortable over it.
(5) Follow feelings in regard to intervals ; if tired by long
    ones have a snack between meals.
(6) If you have to work all day have your heaviest meal
    in the evening.
(7) Have rest before a meal. Don't eat a big meal when
    tired.
(8) Do not try and have a whole diet absorbable, some
    roughage is needed.

I have chapter and verse on my patients' cards for all this,
and the research showing the extra vim given by fresh food
against stale. If you can eat only a little, let that little have

[1] This has happened since I wrote the above. I found cyder suitable
in one case.

a good vitamin content.   Remember feeding is a vital business.
We are dealing with biology, lists of calories and contents are
useful but Nature works with the biomorphs, not on pure
chemistry and physics.

If you boil your baby's milk he will have rickets because
he does not get the live cells he needs and the biomorphs.
Live food is our natural food when young.

As you get older you want less carbohydrates, less milk,
and you have to go back to the shorter-interval feeding of
early childhood.

If a child has a fad about not eating some article of diet it
is probably right.   Again and again I have tested this and
found the child right and the anxious mother wrong.   As we
get older our tastes get more vicious.   In early childhood our
instincts are usually sound, particularly as regards avoiding
things.

Statistics might be compiled on diets for various conditions,
but I doubt if the labour would be worth it.

To all those who use the oscilloclast or any form of testing
circuit I would strongly urge food testing ; it is always a
benefit.   In many cases a source of real trouble is found,
quite unexpectedly.   With a little practice 50 or 60 tests
can be made in fifteen minutes.   Dieting in many cases is as
important as medicine.

ALUMINIUM POISONING.

Connected with dieting is the subject of cooking.   Copper
poisoning was recognised many years ago and in many cases
copper pots with tin linings have been replaced by aluminium.
Over thirty years ago I purchased aluminium pots in Bombay ;
these were made by being hammered out by hand.   I used
some of these for eighteen years in India, and I think one or
two survived later.   I now find I have been suffering from
aluminium poisoning myself, although I have banished aluminium from the home for some time.

One cannot, however, avoid the effect of aluminium cooking-
pots as one has meals outside one's own home, for aluminium
is in common use for cooking vessels.   I note now that dining
out frequently means an upset of some sort.   I think probably
that the machine-made pots are more dangerous than the old
beaten-out kind.   It is obvious that the metal in a pot which
is made by one punch from a sheet undergoes a different
process of strain from that which is hammered out.   My
attention was first drawn to aluminium poisoning by articles

in American journals. I then tried a series of experiments, boiling up vegetables in aluminium and in iron pots ; meat, fruit and eggs were also included, always with a control. I did not add alkali nor did I re-cook meat or vegetables. Only in the case of eggs did I constantly get an increase of aluminium. There is something in the eggshell which acts on aluminium and sets free particles which penetrate the egg.

When I have been taking personal rates from patients aluminium has hardly ever turned up, though I must have tested a large number of people who had aluminium present in their tissues. Why is this ? I think it must be because aluminium dead material. I have found *B. welchii* frequently enough, and *welchii* is generally present with aluminium poisoning. Early in December, 1931, I heard a paper by Dr. R. M. Le Hunte Cooper on aluminium poisoning (*see Homœopathic Journal*, Jan., 1932). While I was hearing him speak I could remember symptoms among my own patients which pointed to aluminium as a cause. I also found aluminium in persons whom I had not suspected of suffering from its effects.

Every kind of soil produces its own flora. An aluminium soil is closely connected with *B. welchii*. I cannot go so far as to say that aluminium produces a *B. welchii* infection, but as all my aluminium cases have had this form of infection it looks like it. Further, aluminium added to a normal reacting blood, but one which is sensitive to aluminium, produces an altered wave on 70,703, which is the P.R. for *welchii*.

To investigate what happens when a few grains of aluminium are added to a sensitive system I added a very small quantity in the circuit to my own serum. I had previously cleared myself of aluminium by taking aluminium 30-c for about a week. Each reaction before it was taken with aluminium was measured and found equal to 37±. The results of testing with aluminium were as follows :—

(Brackets indicate that the first number was put on the first rheostat and second brackets on second rheostat.)

Stomach 74 ± +	Brain 21 + +
Small intestine 74 ± +	Thyroid 37 + −
Cæcum 74 ± +	Pineal 37 + −
Appendix 70 ± +	Thymus 37 + −
Ascending colon 74 ± +	Parathyroid 37 + −
Descending colon 74 ± +	Ant. pituitary 74 + +
Rectum 21 + +	Post. pituitary 74 + +
(Rectum) (vagus) 21 + +	Adrenal cortex 37 + −
(Rectum)(sympathetic) 21 + +	Adrenal medulla 37 + −

Liver 10 + +
Pancreas 1 + 73 —
Skin 74 ± +
Lens of eye 37 + —
Optic nerve 37 + —
Spleen 21 + +

Testicle 37 + —
Prostate 37 + —
Bone 28 + +
Heart 37 + —
Knee-joint 37 + —
Striped muscle 37 + —
Tendon 37 + —

Put into plain words, the above table means that aluminium excites an increased activity in stomach and bowels but paralyses the action of the rectum and lowers the action of the liver, spleen and pancreas and brain, increasing action of skin and pituitary. The symptom of flatulence is accounted for by the presence of *B. welchii*, which is a gas-forming organism.

I recognise aluminium on its atomic weight, 26·96. If I get an excess above normal and positive reactions on both sides of the abdomen it may be due to the metal, in which case the reaction does not repeat ; if due to a live organism it does. In either case I am suspicious of aluminium absorption.

I have shown experimentally what we might expect from aluminium : firstly, diarrhœa from over-excitement of the stomach and guts, and when this is over constipation from inability to pass soft stools. This is typical. I am quoting not only from my own experience but from the evidence of Cooper and a number of others. The stools passed are pale and soft.

The next most common symptom is weariness, lack of power in nervous system from brain downwards. This loss of power is important for the worker and renders him open to infections he might otherwise be resistant to. Aluminium depresses the pancreas—a very important item in resisting power to bacterial invasion. According to my experiments pancreatic secretion has greater bacterial resisting power than any secretion from other glands. My own experience and that of patients shows that a dose of aluminium opens one to effects or so-called " chill," which usually means invasion by various bowel and catarrhal organisms. It is this lowering of resistance and brain-power which is really the most serious charge against aluminium.

There are, I have no doubt, a fairly large number of people who can stand a good dose of aluminium, but there are also a very large number who can't do so. I have, between December 1931, and June, 1934, come across 50 cases of aluminium absorption. I will not call all these cases poisoning because that suggests something more acute than was present in every case. But in all these cases aluminium absorption formed an important item. Every case seen, since treatment, has started to clear out aluminium from the system and has improved ; in some cases the improvement has been very remarkable.

In these 50 cases bone invasion was present in four, constipation or diarrhœa or both alternately in all in varying degrees ; lack of energy was a symptom in all cases. One curious symptom in the joint cases is that lesions are always referred to as very slight traumatisms. The patient says : " I twisted my knee," or sometimes " I think I must have twisted my knee." This is due to slackened ligaments.

I have been asked several times : Does aluminium cause cancer ? One patient pointed out that cancer had markedly increased during the period aluminium had come into common use and bowel disease had increased during this period also. I have no evidence that aluminium causes cancer ; it has sufficient crimes without that. It may, however, produce a type of bowel irritation which prepares the gut for cancer. In three cases aluminium was apparently the cause of a return of cancer toxæmia.

It is necessary in trying to repair the damage done by aluminium to clear each system of the poison. A normal reaction for aluminium on spleen or a spot of blood is not sufficient ; the known organs and nervous system must be separately tested.

Until aluminium has entirely been given up for cooking utensils we shall never be free of the risk of this form of poisoning. Cooper has shown by gross chemical tests that aluminium can be absorbed by eggs, vegetables and other foodstuffs. Those who have followed me thus far will realise that the worst danger from aluminium does not come from such amounts of aluminium as a chemist can demonstrate. The element in gross portions may simply pass through the canal with the stools in a person who does not readily dissolve and digest the metal. Such a person might escape aluminium poisoning. When the foodstuffs have become impregnated with the ions of aluminium, a colloid solution of aluminium has been formed which is in a ready state for absorption. Leaden bullets have been tolerated in the tissues for years without harm, but a moderate amount of colloidal lead means lead poisoning.

It has been suggested that the public will not listen to this story of aluminium poisoning unless they can hear of considerable quantities of aluminium being recovered from foodstuffs. People of that kind undoubtedly exist, but the law of the survival of the fittest is likely to cause a reduction in the numbers of those who take so limited a view.

I have no doubt at all that aluminium is doing a grave amount of harm among the population at large and is probably causing us a serious loss of work energy. There can be no doubt at all that it inflicts grave injury on a number of people. Possibly the character of the water supply has an effect. I am told that experiments have been made on dogs and that the dogs were no worse. I have measured up two constipated dogs. Both suffered from aluminium absorption. Dogs can be affected by aluminium. It is no answer to say that certain animals were not affected. That is possible, but animals vary like individuals, and in any experiment done I should like to know details. The real danger, I repeat, is not so much from gross particles as from a colloid solution in the food, and anyone who cannot understand this is ignorant of life processes.

The question now arises : What pans shall we buy ? This requires an immediate answer, but experiments must be made before it can be answered satisfactorily. At present, I advise people to revert to enamel or steel pots ; but maybe there is something better and safer.

Let me enumerate again the prominent symptoms of aluminium poisoning : Occasional attacks of diarrhœa, pale stools, constipation with soft stools, pains in joints suggesting strains, rashes, tender spots much affected by cold and damp ; above all, easy exhaustion, pain in liver, spleen and region of cæcum and lower end of descending colon. Four points of pain in abdomen at its corners : cæcum, liver, splenic flexure of colon, cæco-rectal flexure, occasionally pain actually in rectum itself. The experimental reactions I have enumerated vary in individuals, but they all occur in greater or less degree in every case.

As regards treatment, I give aluminium 6 c three times daily for a fortnight or three weeks, till all signs of excess have disappeared. It is usually necessary to treat for the *welchii* infection at the same time.

CHAPTER XIX

COLOUR

I USE colour as an additional treatment to drugs and vibrations occasionally by itself. There is sometimes a stage after a severe illness where a state of balance as regards drugs and internal secretions has been reached but there is no strength in the patient or enjoyment in life ; in such cases colour is invaluable.

Colour means life ; we can recognise this by the look of a human being or a plant. The various colours which come from the sun are in our bodies ; as a rule sunlight is good for us but too much can be deadly, especially to those who have not got protective pigment. Sun-bathing in properly graduated doses is good, but we do not necessarily need all the rays of the spectrum with the ultra-violet and ultra-red rays. What we need when we are really ill are the colours in which we are deficient.

The colours which our bodies give off are invisible to the ordinary eye, but they can be seen by sensitives and they can be measured just as visible colours can be measured. Invisible rays are presumably of considerably shorter wavelength than visible, but I have not succeeded in proving this ; all I can say is that the red band in the aura causes a harder reflex with 34,500 ohms than with 345 ohms. The actual intensity as measured in the secondary circuit is the same with 34,500 or 345.

When a red film is used which gives a 345 reaction it is very difficult to distinguish between the effects of 345 and 34,500.

Colour		Ohms		Representative colour wave length in microns
Violet	..	109,999	..	0·41
Blue	..	99,100	..	0·47
Green	..	76,500	..	0·52
Yellow	..	56,6·0	..	0·58
Orange	..	48,600	..	0·60
Red	..	34,500	..	0·65

The preceding table gives the wave-lengths expressed in ohms of a series of colours. The wave-length in microns of the best representative of the colour is also given ; this figure is taken from Hodgman-Lange Handbook, 13th edition. The filters used by me were perhaps not the most representative of the colour as I was limited in choice and had to use one or more filters which gave the purest blue, red or yellow.

What we learn from this table is that the colour with the shorter wave-length causes a reaction on higher ohmage. Therefore to produce a shorter wave-length we must use higher ohmage.

The repeat action every 100 ohms makes it difficult to get correspondence between ohms and microns ; further, though invisible waves are probably of shorter wave-length than the visible spectrum, we cannot be certain they may be repeat waves in the ultra-red which would be equally invisible to our eyes. For the present we have to be satisfied with what we have got, that the invisible rays in the aura or emanating from persons will cause a reflex on the same ohmage as visible colours, and the small amount of evidence we have, i.e. hardness of reflex with higher ohmage, suggests that the invisible ray is of shorter wave-length.

The colour centre in the cerebrum gives a H.I.F. 93,540. This can be felt over the pineal in the centre of the head between the ears, but a better reflex is obtained on Abrams' S.V. area between the eyes where the pituitary is best measured.

Over the pineal area 93,540 = 11,111, on the pituitary area = 22,222, if I tune on a second rheostat to pineal on its area I get an intensity of 22,222, but if I tune to pituitary I get 33,333, which appears to show what colour-vision is more closely connected with the pituitary.

The general visualisation centre gives the best reaction over the pineal on 82.160. With coils at 45° 82,160 = 23,333 on pineal area. If we tune with pineal number on 2nd rheostat on pineal area I get an off-scale reaction with coils at 90°. Tuning with pituitary number on pituitary area gives an intensity of 23,333 with coils at 45°, so that pineal appears to be the gland affected by visualisation. It is increased in its action when a clairvoyant starts visualising.

During the examination of a patient by a clairvoyant he reported that there was an abnormal colouration over the sex organs. He showed me the colour by putting together two filters which produced a brownish yellow colour. These two filters had a good effect on the patient and one of the waves they gave off in considerable intensity was 72,954, the H.I.F. of caladium, a drug which is often useful for the oversexed and others in whom the sex centre in the brain is unbalanced owing to infection of the sex organs.

When certain areas are affected clairvoyants can see an alteration in colour and to secure balance this is often the colour to use.

The inner layer of the human aura causes a reaction on 99,100 ohms, i.e. blue ; the next layer on 34,500, i.e. red ; the next on 48,600 orange, and the 4th on 56,600, yellow, this goes out to 12½ inches ; between 14 and 15 inches in my own aura I get a Wratten red 29 reaction and just outside this a narrow band of orange.

Some persons who have gifts of healing give off colour rays which are in excess of those present in ordinary individuals, or at any rate they can do so at will till the power is exhausted.

I have measured up four different healers—all gave off more than one colour-wave and one gave three.

One of them gave off a blue and a violet wave ; he treated me over an injured spot. This spot on examination was deficient in blue, normal in violet. After he had treated for a few minutes I measured him again and found his violet supply had not altered, but his blue, which was in excess before, was now the normal body level. I had been brought up to normal.

Another friend of mine gave off green and violet and I examined two cases he had treated. In one case he had reduced his own supply below normal in raising the patient to normal.

I should judge that only short treatments were needed ; this healer had been very successful in several cases.

I do not know if the colours are the actual remedy or a mere concomitant, but seeing what can be done with a lamp and filter I think one may conclude they play an important part in healing.

Some people tell you it is life-force that heals naturally ; it is this, but one wants to know what sort of life-force.

Again I am told that the healer is a mere agent for transmitting life-force. Again I may agree, that is probably true of everything we do, but channels vary in effectiveness.

Had I time and opportunity I think I should be able to show that the possessors of certain colours were best for certain classes of cases.

Colours balance on 37 ohms just as other waves do in the human body.

Colour, as I have shown in the chapter on the Aura, is always connected with life forces. Colour likes and dislikes are, I

think, closely connected with character. The east and south
of Europe are more colourful than this somewhat drab country,
although the vivid and various greens of England are a
grateful contrast to the grey-greens of the Australian gum
forests. Men in England are restrained by custom from
indulging in colours, more's the pity ; Puritanism banished
colour from our clothes. Practical necessity has reduced our
troops to wearing khaki. Real benefit to health can be got
through the eye if you are capable of appreciating colours.
Mr. W. F. Froetas, an artist and engineer in South Africa,
sent me some sketches in colour scales to try out on patients.
I have experimented with them. The patient selected the
sketch she liked best ; while looking at the picture all her
reactions altered for the better. This was not due to radio-
activity from the picture as the effect went when the eyes
were closed. You can treat yourself when down if you love
colour and have imagination. There are two pictures I can
always enjoy in memory : the vivid green of an Indian rice-
field, with darker green of the palm trees on the neighbouring
bund of the bank from which it was irrigated, then against
a grey monsoon sky there is a gold mohur tree whose scarlet
and yellow streaked blossoms stand out as a glorious patch of
colour. There was another gold mohur tree in our compound
in Madras against a bank of green which carries very happy
memories when the boys were small and the world went very
well indeed. A dog lives by smells they say ; surely man
lives by his eyes to appreciate form and colour. When form
leaves us colour must remain. It is the essence of life.

Clairvoyants tell us our personal auric colours alter with
emotion ; they say anger is red—it feels like it.

Over-active people often need blue or green. Now we
will consider the use of a lamp and filters, the more prosaic
method I have to use, for I have not the time to give colour
in any other way.

I was introduced to colour treatment by Dr. Dobson Hessey.
He used filters but he also got the patient to think of colours
and he concentrated himself on colours. This method is
effective, but I fancy Hessey was a bit clairvoyant as to his
test of colours. When I came to use his method I found it
would not always work with me and took up too much time.
Colour treatment is a complicated business. Consider the
following tables ; every organ in the body is affected differently, every organism has its likes and dislikes. Different
stages of infection need different colours. Abrams treated
tubercular patients with yellow, but if their lungs were affected

this was possibly wrong, because yellow lowers the activity
of lung tissue.

There is only one safe rule : use the colour which raises
the vitality of the whole patient.

EFFECT OF COLOUR ON ORGANS.

Organs		Increased by	Decreased by
Orchitic ext.	.. ..	Red	Blue
Ovarian ext.	.. ..	Blue	Red
Thyroid ..	.. ..	Blue	Red
Parathyroid ext.	.. ..	Red	Blue
Adrenal cortex	.. ..	Red	Yellow
Adrenalin ..	.. ..	Yellow	Red
Anterior pituitary	..	Blue	Red
Post. pituitary	.. ..	Red	Blue
Pineal ..	.. ..	Yellow	Green
Thymus ..	.. ..	Green	Yellow
Liver ..	.. ..	Green	Blue
Lungs ..	.. ..	Red	Yellow
Kidney ..	.. ..	Yellow	Blue
Bone.. ..	.. ..	Yellow	Green
Cerebral ..	.. ..	Yellow	Green
Prostate ..	.. ..	Green	Blue
Mammary ..	.. ..	Yellow	Green
Pancreas ..	.. ..	Red	Green

EFFECT OF COLOURS ON MICRO-ORGANISMS.

Organism	Frequency	Activity increased by	Decreased by
B. tuberculosis (Koch) ..	57,732	Blue	Yellow
B. proteus	33,499	Green	Yellow
B. morgan	97,979	Green	Red
S t r e p t o c o c c u s non-hæmolyticus ..	67,188	Green	Red
Streptococcus fæcalis ..	26,677	Green	Red
Streptococcus hæmolyticus	77,610	Green	Red
Streptococcus rheumaticus	65,061	Yellow	Blue
Staphylococcus aureus ..	48,889	Yellow, green	Blue
B. tetanus	41,124	Red	Green
Micrococcus melitensis ..	14,604	Blue	Yellow
B. typhosus..	41,988	Blue	Green
B. bach. No. 7	38,231	Green	Orange
B. mutabilis	91,105	Green	Red
Paratyphosis A	38,978	Green	Red
Fæcalis alcaligenes.. ..	98,989	Green	Purple
Dysentery type (non-lactose)	78,788	Yellow	Purple
Pneumococcus Type 1 ..	35,301	Blue	Yellow
Gonococcus	34,688	Red	Green
Micrococcus catarrhalis ..	15,886	Orange	Green
B. coli	98,591	Blue	Red

For every human being a colour can be found which will
do them more good than any other colour, and this is the one
to give them.   In their ordinary state of health this is constant,
only when they depart markedly from normal is another
colour needed.

There appears to me to be a connection between personal
colour and the organism the patient tends to grow.   For
instance the person who needs red when he is a bit down tends
to grow B. *morgan* and streptococci.   Everyone appears to
have two colours which do him good under certain circum-
stances ; he is either a red-green man or a blue-yellow, and
the two are colours with similar wave-lengths, the red being
positive and green negative, or yellow positive and blue
negative.

Most people at times need tuning up or toning down.   People
who live too much on their nerves, whose metabolism works
too fast, need blue or green.   Those who need greater activity
of action are benefited by red, orange or yellow.   If you
look at the table showing the action of colours on glands you
will see that red stimulates the male sex gland and blue the
female.   The highest effect on male glands is in the red-orange,
and that on females in indigo blues.   The red end of the
spectrum is positive and the violet end negative.

My own colour filters are Wratten red 29, which give a
positive wave on the left side of the abdomen and a neutral
wave on the right, and Wratten green 58, which causes a
negative wave on the right side of the abdomen and a neutral
wave on the left ; both these give a reaction on 88,960 ohms.
These colour filters are invariably needed at the start of
treatment in cancer.   When the virus is positive Wratten
red 29 is needed; usually when the frequency for the virus 80,441
changes its polarity to neutral, green 58 is needed.   That is
so long as the more active form of vaccine is needed Wratten
red 29 is needed, but sometimes a period with green 58 is
necessary to assist in elimination before another dose of the
more active vaccine is given.

The red filter acts like a vaccine in helping to kill the virus
and the green as an eliminator of toxins.   After green 58 has
done its work there is frequently a stage where a violet filter
is needed ; this gives a frequency on 97,710 ohms.   This
filter I have labelled U.V. as it was made for Lord Clifford
of Chudleigh to represent ultra-violet on corresponding wave-
lengths, presumably corresponding wave in the visible spectrum.   This is needed for some weeks and then the patients
may need their own special filter, or not infrequently a filter
we number as orange 22.

The red, green and violet stages are regular, but the use of red and green in each case is not always the same.

The one important thing in selecting colour is to find the tint that raises vitality in the highest degree. If we have any doubt we try the effect on the Neon lamp described in the chapter on the Aura, or get the patient to go to a distance from the receiving plate in the testing cage and see which tint will expand his aura most.

I always give colour over the episternal notch; in cancer cases I have measured the effect a number of times, when the outside areas were covered with a lead shield and this area exposed to the red 29 colour the virus reaction on 80,441 was brought to normal. When the light was shone on the neck and the area above the episternal notch was covered this did not happen. Even when the site of the growth was irradiated the effect was not so good as over the episternal notch.

There is some very important vital centre here connected with colour, probably connected with the aura. There appears to be no anatomical explanation and I have not had an explanation from any source. Books on occultism place a vital centre over the thyroid but make no mention of this spot.

Micro-organisms give off colour-waves other than those in their aura. I have not been able at present to work on this effect, but the fact was demonstrated by Dr. Geoffrey Hodgson, who has clairvoyant vision. Dr. Bach gave Hodgson some half-dozen solutions of micro-organisms. After about a week's study Bach's laboratory attendant gave Hodgson some numbered tubes; by looking at them Hodgson was able to name each solution correctly. He described three rays of the same colour, one of which continued out straight for a distance and the other two being curved. This clairvoyant method may play a very important part in diagnosis in the future, but it will need much careful work in conjunction with other means of diagnosis for effective use. Every new method needs checking up by other more recognised methods. These colour-waves which enabled Hodgson to correctly name solutions which were to the ordinary eye colourless water, may correspond with the H.I.F. I get from them.

It must be noted that these waves of colour seen by a clairvoyant were given off from solutions of dead cultures. They were not due to life other than such life as pertains to minerals. There is a great field for observation and experiment in regard to colours from elements and compounds. Colour visible and invisible plays an important part in our lives and it is not necessary to use lamps of great power in giving colour treatment. My lamp is 250 watts. In twenty minutes I normalised a Morgan infection measuring 74++, which indicates the presence of an active bacillus using Wratten red 29.

The use of ultra-violet lamps appears to me to need great care. I was told of one case where a man had been treated for an inflammatory condition of the ear ; this was cured, but the auditory nerve was so damaged that the patient became completely deaf.

The body is a delicate machine and does not require gross agents for its treatment.

It is a form of mental materialism to consider that mass doses or violent mechanical remedies are necessary for treatment ; when one grasps the fact that cases can be markedly benefited by quite gentle means, such as colour or a few drops of a simple tincture, or a low potency, one feels less and less inclined to expose a patient to the more active forms of radiation, although these in their proper place and under skilled direction may have wonderful effects. So too can high potencies, but one does not want to use them all the time.

CHAPTER XX

THE OSCILLOCLAST

I

ABRAMS' vibratory treatment apparatus, which he called the oscilloclast or wave-breaker, was described in some detail in Abrams' " Diagnosis and Treatment " which included a report by Professor Taylor Jones. A further description was given by Drs. Perkins and Parkes in " The Detection of Disease," published as recently as 1930. It does not seem necessary to repeat this.

The oscilloclast itself has a rocking make-and-break movement, and when the apparatus is attached to the electric main, a series of alternating oscillations are sent along a wire to the treatment-unit which controls the particular set of vibrations sent to the patient. The Abrams' treatment-unit had three sets of tuning studs, all three wound in a similar way. Each set had ten studs ; the first was wound roughly, equivalent to 100 ohms, the tenth to 1,000 ohms, and the intervening studs were approximately at equal intervals. Those who use the original apparatus can, therefore, give combinations of ten different waves.

Before Abrams died he had apparently recognised that this was hardly a sufficient variety, and introduced what he called the micro-oscilloclast unit which enabled fractional waves to be given, filling in the intervals.

For some time most of Abrams' followers used all three sets of dials, but Dr. Hayward introduced the plan of working out what he called a " personal rate " for each patient which would raise all vitality waves and normalise all disease waves.

If you are going to use the oscilloclast alone this wave must raise endocrines to 37 ohms, cause the general body tuning to equal 49,000 ohms positively, negatively and neutrally, raise the biomorphs to 111,111 ohms and cause all disease waves to register at 37 ohms. If you can find a setting to do this you have the simillimum of the homœopath. Once you have started working on these lines you will find it far easier to obtain one rate which will secure normality than three separate waves which will work together.

The original Abrams' idea was to treat one disease frequency at a time, or at most three, and the three most prominent were selected. 100 ohms was the treatment for malaria (or 32 ohms), staphylococcus 34 or 35 ohms, 200 ohms for streptococcus (or 60 ohms), 300 ohms for syphilis (or 55 and 57), 400 ohms for gonorrhœa (or 52 ohms), 500 ohms for tubercle (or 42 ohms), 600 ohms for cancer (or 50 ohms).

Undoubtedly results were obtained, but when one considers that there is no specific for these conditions and that every case needs different treatment and that it is hardly too much to say that no two cases are ever exactly alike and probably never will be, it is rather marvellous that good results did ensue.

The explanation is that Abrams was really working on approximately like waves. His original rates were absolutely empirical. He and his engineers simply set themselves to find out windings to annul those conditions which he recognised under the above headings. It has never been explained why these particular windings should have been used for these particular conditions. It was, as I say, arrived at by Abrams purely empirically.

Anyone who has studied those particular conditions known by the names of tuberculosis, cancer, asthma, and syphilis, knows perfectly well that there is no specific treatment for any one disease, not even when due to any one particular organism. This is more especially the case in chronic diseases.

One can, however, understand that when working on wavelengths one special tuning can be found to normalise another special tuning. No one has ever tried to show why a 400-ohms tuning should normalise 52 ohms tuning.

The higher the ohmage you use the more complicated the field you produce.

Dr. Martha Petree has made a special study of the oscilloclast. She found that as ohmage was increased the field of action was increased. It was, to a certain point, a simple sum in mathematics : 1,000 contains more possibilities of variations than a 100 ; 100,000 than a 1,000. Petree found, as she went on increasing ohmage, that she could treat more disease conditions with the same number. The beneficial effects were not shown as a steady climb upwards. There were positions on the rheostats which were markedly less effective, but as she went on the beneficial tunings got more numerous, and at 98,545 ohms she got a tuning which was universally beneficial, not necessarily the best for everyone, but a tuning which would aid everybody and cover a very wide field indeed.

She had reached a point where she was treating the patient as a patient and not specially striking at any one particular condition.

I have found that this line of treatment will always work in with any set of drugs or with colour, and I have never known it interfere with anything else. This does not mean that this is the best treatment wave for everyone, but if you had to treat a patient in a hurry you could not go wrong using this treatment wave.

Personally I think exact tuning is very important, and that one ought to use at least five figures. The last figure may make all the difference. It is better to have high ohmage, but you can get good effects with lower so long as you secure accuracy of tuning, i.e. you could use 985·45 ohms in place of 98,545 ohms. Accuracy of tuning is most important ; a decimal place altered makes all the difference. For instance, if you put indium in the testing circuit you get a personal rate for it on 88,061 ohms or 880·61 ohms ; if you test for scrophularia nodosa you get 88,060 ohms. The clinical effects of indium and scrophularia are quite different, and so are the effects of 88,061 and 88,060.

You may object, of course, that the plant and element give off many different waves besides those quoted ; they do, but so do the oscilloclast settings. The waves set up by the 88,060 ohms are not simple either. Practically I find that if I want 88,060, 88,061 is of no use and may be less than useful. This has been noted by others as well as by myself. There was an article in the *Electronic Research Journal* some years back on the necessity for careful tuning and showing how a faulty setting of one decimal point by a careless assistant spoilt the result of treatment.

Some years ago I was in the treatment room of a colleague and he asked me to prescribe a setting for a tubercular patient with a very rapid pulse—130. On going into the history I came to the conclusion that the pulse was probably due to an intestinal toxin. I advised treating with 182·11 as this is a frequency common to many intestinal organisms. In a minute or two the pulse was 100 and the patient remarked on her increased comfort. I was able to alter the tuning slightly without the patient seeing what I was doing, as the apparatus was behind her. In a very short space, perhaps a minute, she complained that her discomfort had returned. The pulse was again 130. Correcting the tuning caused an almost immediate sense of comfort and a pulse-rate of 100.

This is really common sense. If you want a good effect

with your wireless set you take some trouble with your tuning You do not expect good audition by having it set more or less right ; it has to be just so. 182·11 is the molecular weight of mannite, which is affected by most intestinal organisms. I do not say that this is a treatment for a rapid pulse, but it is a logical wave to use for intestinal toxæmia if you have no time to test.

I ask those who are working with the oscilloclast to work out a personal rate for each patient. Alter it by a fraction and note the changes due to alteration. If we find that the patient's P.R. is 98,548 and this = 74 negative, and we give this wave, we have a logical method of treatment and a defence against critics. We can say that we are giving a similar wave to the one which we find defective, i.e. seriously unbalanced, and that we find, on testing, that this wave will increase the activity of the lowered endocrines, depress those which are in excess, normalise those waves which are unbalanced, due to invasion, and raise general body-tuning to normal. We have then an unanswerable position if our tests are accepted.

As regards secondary tuning, I think we might have still higher ohmage and we cannot be too accurate. As for the oscilloclast itself, probably something better could be made. Opinions seem to differ with regard to the wave-length given off ; Taylor Jones reports finding that the frequency of the oscillation corresponds to a wave-length of about 50 metres. Boyd and Mr. Gavin agree with Taylor Jones' findings. Other findings have been obtained in America. We need, first of all, to settle what is the average wave-length given off by the human body. Englund, in the Bell Telephone Laboratories, worked out his own body wave-length at 3·688 metres. I wonder if an absolutely healthy body should not be 3·7 metres. The body probably gives off a number of different wave-lengths, 3·7 may be one. It is quite possible that we give off quite long waves as well as very minute ones. I fancy that a number of the waves we are testing are to be measured in decimal points of microns. A suitable instrument for treatment would be one which was accurately based on some human wave-length. It is hardly possible that a highly complicated apparatus like the human body should not give off an extremely varied number of wave-lengths.

We are, I think, only just at the beginning of radio treatment, and as soon as physicists and physicians can get over a childish prejudice against new ideas we shall go ahead with rapidity, but we must set a face of flint against suggestions of something mysterious, " tapping Mother Earth," " powers of electricity " and vague statements suggesting " God-given powers of healing." All means of healing are God-given, yes ! even castor oil. Oscilloclast treatment is like anything else, most excellent when used with skill. That so much good was done by Abrams and others using his somewhat crude methods, points to there being a beneficial effect from mere attachment to the machine. Taylor Jones reports that attachment to any setting raises and lowers the patient's potential about 200 times a minute. This may in itself be beneficial. Patients have described a buoyancy for a number of hours afterwards and reported that it suddenly departed about eight or nine hours after treatment. But this kind of general tonic benefit is hardly worth labour and money simply by itself ; it can be got in easier ways, but it may be used as a foundation for permanent benefit if the treatment be specific for the patient.

II

My own method of using the oscilloclast is to give the highest intensity frequency of the drugs which I gave as drainage drugs at 6-c. These are negative when given by the oscilloclast and correspond to the 6-c preparation in polarity. If you give a positive preparation by mouth and use the oscilloclast with the same frequency, one treatment neutralises the other. I never use the oscilloclast more than twice a week. My instrument is stepped up by being given through a valve set similar to the one I use in the diagnostic set. Occasionally I meet with a person who cannot be treated in this way, but seldom with one who cannot take colour. The vast majority of patients like oscilloclast treatment and after a short experience ask to be allowed to have it in addition to drug treatment. Only in very rare cases have I obtained effects anything like that due to high potencies ; effects are gradual. It is an effective addition to treatment but does not replace high potencies. It should be possible to get very rapid effects by the use of different valves, but I see no particular gain in using an instrument for half an hour or so when an equal or better effect can be got by taking a high potency. For gradual treatment the oscilloclast is excellent.

CHAPTER XXI

THOUGHT FORMS

THEIR EFFECT ON THE TESTING CIRCUIT

IT has usually been considered that the use of the human indicator in the testing circuit was a weakness. There is nothing in the way of mechanism that one can think of that has not got weak points. The perfect engine, the perfect system of wireless, does not exist.

The human body is the most delicate mechanism that exists for testing atomic changes and the best for testing such changes in human beings, but this very delicacy, this sensitiveness to thought, can be a disadvantage. It is a disadvantage in studying pure physics. But physics is not our main aim ; we are studying life in all its aspects.

Since the human detector and the operator can be affected by thought, this is obviously a difficulty when testing under some mental strain such as the excitement of public tests or over-anxiety as to result of test regarding, say, a relative. Thought may also affect research work. This, however, enters into all research work to a certain extent ; it certainly enters into ordinary medical work, and indeed business and all human affairs. It really comes down to this : that the use of the circuit with certainty largely depends on the skill of the operator and his knowledge of the difficulties he is up against.

To know what one is dealing with is most essential. This is one reason for my undertaking a number of experiments in regard to the effect of thought. A second reason was that all knowledge is useful and a study of thought-forms interesting. A third reason is that a school of workers has arisen in America led by Dr. MacRoberts, who think they work entirely on emanations and that physical electrons have no effect on the human reflexes.

MacRoberts and others have had most curious experiences, and some of the group are certainly clairvoyant. I have a great respect for MacRoberts' work and character, but I think he is obviously wrong here. Man is acted on by physical

electrons and thought electrons.   To suggest that all my results
are due to electrons on a different plane from the electrons
in mineral and in the human body stirs feelings in me akin
to those of Alice when the Red King suggested that she was
merely part of his dream.

Abrams' genius picked out the finest instrument going, but
this fine instrument has deceived many of Abrams' followers.
For a long time I was deceived myself, and got considerably
mixed up over the behaviour of the thought-world overlying
the physical.   It is only after a series of careful tests that I
have, I think, unravelled the mix-up.

The tale of my investigations begins at Chicago.   For some
time before this I had obtained reflexes for disease from
photos, I had obtained them for minerals from photos, I had
worked out reactions for structures from photos occasionally
and found them correct when I tested actual structures.   In
September, 1928, I was reading a paper in Chicago.   I met
there Dr. MacRoberts.   One evening, after we had discussed
mutual interests in our work and had some small argument,
MacRoberts said :   " Now, doctor, I will show you something."
MacRoberts asked me to lie down and concentrate on the
personality of a patient.   Then, using his mechanical subject,
" Streborcam," he worked out some details about three
patients of whom I thought in succession.   The information
he gave me afterwards proved correct in all three cases ; some
of it I knew already, other facts I was ignorant of.   One
patient had a toixn from a parasite I had never heard of.
The third case was the most striking.

He told me that this patient had lost a tooth—he indicated
the site—that there was a 55 reaction on the gum, that there
was a metal reaction and that the trouble was almost certainly
due to extraction with dirty forceps.   This proved to be
correct ; a very severe swelling had occurred after extraction.
MacRoberts' point was that if you pictured accurately the
whole person any detail would be worked out.   This he
did successfully.

For some time I was unable to follow this up, but study of
the subject seemed desirable.   In February 1930 I got a
colleague to concentrate on a mutual friend whose condition
we knew something about and whom I could check up on.
He thought of a lady who had died of cancer.   He did not say
of whom he was thinking.   I got a cancer reaction clearly.
A few days later he concentrated at an agreed time on his
wife, doing so in his room about two miles away from mine.
I got a reaction 103,063 for one of her personal recognition

numbers which never change. This proved correct. The chances against working this out by fluke are fairly considerable. I then tried thinking of known objects whilst writing their names and working out the reactions from paper. I thought of pennyroyal, its appearance as a plant and its properties, whilst writing the name on paper. When the paper was placed in the dynamizer I got a reaction 33,356, which I afterwards proved to be the best P.R. for the drug.

Some time passed before I checked up the actual drug and took a P.R. I then got 33,356 for pennyroyal. I found I could get reactions for structures, drugs and parasites from words in books if I thought about them with good visualisation. MacRoberts describes a method of selecting remedies for his patients by the reactions from words. He has a special apparatus attached to his circuit for so doing.

I found that it was possible to select a drug for a patient by running down a list of words connected to the circuit by a piece of wire attached to the circuit. I did this several times, and then the method failed.

One very striking instance was a case in which I selected dirca for a patient by this method. I obtained a reaction for 83,704 as a P.R. for the patient. I found that this reaction was not in our list. I got a list of drugs and passed a pointer attached to a wire down the list with 83,704 on the rheostats. When I came to the word " dirca " I got a reaction on my subject. I repeated this with my eyes shut—it worked just the same. I then sent for a preparation of dirca and on testing it suited my patient very well. The drug was sent to him and did him a considerable amount of good. I had no knowledge of dirca ; I had not even heard of the drug at the time, so that though I had my patient in my mind at the time it was impossible for me to connect this word with him. When I looked up the drug in Clarke's dictionary it seemed a suitable drug for him.

It is worth while considering in detail this curious mental phenomenon, for it gives us a key to what happens. When we were testing the list of words to find out what corresponded with 83,704 I had no blood in the circuit, merely these figures on the rheostats. I was thinking of my patient more or less unconsciously and the reaction was clear and good. When we got a potency of dirca the P.R. worked out at 83,704. This and other reaction numbers I am quite unable to carry in my head for many minutes together ; my subject can remember figures well but he cannot see what I am doing when I am tuning in to a preparation. We did not therefore get the

P.R. for dirca itself as 83,704 because I had previously got it from print. This tale may seem rather incredible to some people, but I have to tell it because it illustrates very well on the one hand how one can be taken in and how, on the other, quite incredible things may happen. When at another sitting we examined the word dirca in print it gave no reaction at all more than the other words. Was the whole occurrence then a dream ? Was I mistaken in thinking I got a reaction ? Not at all ; I got the reaction all right. What then is the explanation ?

There are two explanations and I prefer the simplest. One is that I was for the time being clairvoyant, which still leaves us foggy., The other is quite understandable. We have found by experiment that when the human mind thinks of anything at all intensely or, even better, by unconscious concentration, a change in chemistry results. We know nothing of this, we do not need to know anything. We think of fear, and we register lowered cortex of the adrenals or some element acted on by fear. We think of lead and we get an altered reaction for lead ; we think of cancer and we get altered lead reactions and others. We do not need to know anything about the connection between cancer, lead, copper, samarium, etc., the altered reactions follow.

Dirca in print started certain vibrations in my unconscious brain ; these passed along my finger to my subject's abdomen and caused a reaction on 83,704. I knew nothing of dirca ; I had never consciously seen the word before. When in good form and unconsciously thinking of my patient I have repeated this feat, but not often ; usually I am too self-conscious.

These experiments were repeated several times ; good visualisation gave accurate information. It was difficult to separate thought-forms from actual reactions. At this stage I talked things over with a medical colleague. We agreed that it was desirable when writing on this subject to keep nothing back ; at the same time it was desirable to clearly investigate how reactions occurred : what was real or, shall we say, what was due to chemical changes ; what was due to thought-forms. For all we know thought-forms may be as real as the other. Thought may be the one permanent thing, more permanent than our bodies. We need not enter into this, but it was desirable at any rate to distinguish one from the other. Since many physicians prescribe for their patients on mental symptoms it seemed possible that if a mental symptom could be transferred to paper by writing it should give a reaction for a drug connected with that symptom.

I will give the list with some comments ; on the whole the resulting reactions are reasonable and could not be due to chance.   In addition to obtaining reactions for mental symptoms I also investigated how the reactions got there.   The captions were written on a piece of paper while concentrating on the idea.   The paper was then held in the two hands and concentration on the idea was continued for about thirty seconds.   Every chance for good contact was given.   I endeavoured to think of the idea, but it is possible that some idea of a human example came in, in some cases this was inevitable.   The paper was then put in the dynamiser and a P.R. taken from it.

I have marked some of the reactions with an E as being excellent.   Most of the others are marked R, i.e. reasonable I have left the others blank as the connection was unknown. In several cases the results are not what I would have chosen as the best representative of the idea, but most of them applied to patients in whom the symptom was apparent and met the particular case which may have been in my mind at the time.

Suspicion	12,717	Sepia	R
Lack of faith..	11,916	Pulsatilla	R
Lack of positivity	62,620	Arsenic alb. ..	R
Lack of grit (can't hold on)	81,711	Cadmium sulph.	E
Despondency	85,530	Mezereum	R
Dread	76,290	Belladonna ..	R
Vacillation	44,080	Staphisgaria	E
Fussiness	71,550	Lilium tigrum	R
Forgetfulness	47,653	Berberis	R
Fuddled head	71,220	Hyoscyamus	R
Hair trigger ..	22,427	Calc. carb. ..	R
Mongolism ..	90,051	Cerato	
Will power	91,522	Hair roots (silica)	E
Overshadowed	56,014	Variolinum and quinine	
Mental inhibition	13,419	Platinum	R
Mental laziness	93,290	Æsculis	R
Slow off the mark ..	85,530	Mezereum	E
Loss of memory	90,346	Rosemary	E
Fidgety (drums with fingers)	22,427	Calc. carb.	R
Always in a hurry, tires others out ; restlessness	77,130	Medorrhinum	E
Self-pity	86,321	Selenium	R

Nick Culpepper says about rosemary : " It helpeth a weak memory and quickeneth the senses."   In Shakespeare's time it was known for its effect on the memory.   Its connection with memory is recognised by modern homœopaths. " Lack of grit, can't hold on," produced the cadmium sulph. P.R. Kent describes a condition in cancer and after severe illness where the patient asks to be let alone and allowed to die. He says he has given cadmium sulphate to such cases, roused them and saved them. I have used cadmium sulph. in despairing cases since I got this reaction with success. Some of our captions are still waiting corresponding drugs.

It would take up too much space to give all the evidence for correspondences ; in some cases there is none, but in most there is an easily recognised connection. In some cases this may have been the subconscious cause for the connection between words and reactions obtained. When I wrote " hair trigger " I was thinking of the person who over-responds to all external stimuli and had nat. mur. in mind but I obtained calc. carb. A faulty calcium metabolism does very often produce this type, and to get a more stable nervous system it is often necessary to correct both the calcium and the chlorine metabolism.

My obtaining the mezereum wave for " Slow off the mark " is certainly interesting, for though I had the drug I knew practically nothing about it. Spurge olive, according to Clarke has, in a case of accidental poisoning, produced loss of vitality and depression bordering on idiocy. He quotes a case cured by daphne mezereum, " Ideas vanish when talking, looks through the window for hours without being conscious of objects around." Clarke gives " slow conception of ideas " as a symptom. This I consider an excellent result, and it was entirely free from conscious knowledge on my part.

During May, 1931, I examined again the question of photographs and X-ray plates. In a number of previous examinations I obtained reactions which appeared to be perfectly correct. For instance, personal rates were taken from structures which proved correct when actual structures were obtained. I had a number of photos which I had previously examined and got clear reactions from them for waves. When examined with no idea of any personality but merely as material the human reactions disappeared. I tried old X-ray plates ; the reactions I had previously obtained were not there. A new X-ray plate of a colleague was obtained who had had a recent fracture. This gave no human balances for reaction for bone or symphytum. I then took reactions from the film, concentrating easily on my friend's personality. I picked up bone and symphytum both unbalanced and other drug reactions which he needed. I then removed the film and tried to obtain reactions by concentration on the patient. It proved most difficult to operate the rheostats, take reflexes and concentrate at the same time ; the reactions came and went. Yet with the X-ray film the concentration was easy. I had no difficulty in obtaining a series of reactions which I later checked up on his serum and found perfectly correct.

What part did the film play ? It was something quite real, for I easily worked out a series of perfectly correct reactions. Moreover, a number of reactions obtained by such methods have been proved perfectly correct. MacRoberts says that thinking a specimen was in the box when it was not he has worked out a perfectly sound diagnosis whilst thinking of the patient. Maybe the film is merely an aid to steady my unconscious attention. He also told me that ideas are imperishable and that an idea in print will give a vibration. My experience is that the printed work aids concentration on the idea and that it is the thought-form that gives the vibration. The book merely gives reaction for paper and printer's ink. When you can get reactions for the ideas you are being slightly clairvoyant.

During April and June, 1931, I made a series of experiments to find out how far writing will pass on thought by radio-activity, and what happens when this is done. It takes up too much space to detail all the experiments and is perhaps dull reading. I have the records. I give here the results :—

(1) If a letter is written with a moderately moist hand sufficient to give contact, the vibrations due to the writer's changes in chemistry while thinking are conveyed to the paper.

(2) If the paper is covered so that the hand does not touch it or the skin is really dry, nothing passes even with purposeful concentration that our circuit could detect except reaction for paper and ink or pencil.

(3) When thoughts causing chemical changes are conveyed to paper, human balances can be measured. Unconscious concentration on an idea is rather more effective than conscious in recording such changes.

(4) Changes of intention during the writing of a letter which were recorded in words showed themselves by changes in polarity of the iron atom in the patient. During the writing of one letter such changes were noted four times.

(5) I found that though a paper which had been written with a protection from the writer's hand gave no reaction by itself, if the idea was thought of I got the reaction. For instance, the sentence " Restlessness tires people out " was written with a consciousness of a certain patient in whom this

was a prominent symptom.   When I thought of her with the paper in the circuit I got a reaction for medorrhinum which corresponds to this symptom.   I then got human balances. That is, the reactions were due to thought by myself not due to the paper which when tested just as a specimen of writing with words unknown gave only ink and paper reactions.

(6) We found that reactions could be obtained perfectly correctly for any substance by writing the name of the substance and thinking about it.   We discovered that the most accurate results were obtained when the substance was accurately visualised.   I tried to visualise ambergris and got a reaction present in that substance.   My subject has actually seen ambergris, and when he visualised and wrote " ambergris " we obtained a reaction which later proved the best P.R. for the drug.

(7) A good visualisation produces a reaction as strong as any produced by a potency itself, and will cross the coils at right angles.

(8) Concentration is greatly aided by some object like a photo or paper holding an idea of the person or thing being concentrated on.

(9) Thinking about an object gave all the chemical details of that object and its condition, either in the present or the past at a certain date.

I have thought of a patient, worked out a series of reactions, obtained the blood and found they were all correct.   There is apparently a thought double of everything that exists. This thought can cause reactions on the human abdomen exactly similar to the material thought about.   Sometimes such experiments work out exactly, then our thoughts have been accurate thoughts.   Sometimes they do not work out, then visualisation has been poor.   We cannot test for things we have never heard of, but we may get reactions in figures for things we have never heard of.   If we concentrate and make a good picture of a human or an object, anyone able to use my circuit and similar ones can pick up details.

In all cases it was found that the use of a written or printed word or a photo enabled a reaction to be obtained much more easily.   Why was this ?   It was not that I was looking at the photo or word.   In some cases the book was before me but I did not look at it.   My subject held the receiving electrode over the word.   In some cases the photo was in the next cage with electrode on the spot to be tested.   In no case could I pay attention to the text or picture.   I was fully occupied taking the reaction ; one hand was stroking

the subject, the other turning the rheostats ; my mind was
thinking of a person, or a worm or plant. Why have the book
or picture or paper at all ? It was not essential, but it eased
things tremendously. If you are an E.R.A. man try it.

Our emanation friends will say : " You own, then, that
something does come from print ? " I reply : " I can't get
a thing from print but paper, graphite and so on, unless I
know what is written on it ; then I can."

How about a clairvoyant ? A clairvoyant, I am told, can
get visions from writing, from stones or personal possessions.
I have good second-hand proof that this is so. Probably
MacRoberts and his followers have this gift. Many women
appear to have a lot of it. Since I can do what I have done, I
am possibly a border-line case, only clairvoyant now and
then. I find it safer to keep my senses on this plane. I have
to use such powers as I have for healing.

I come to the practical effect of this doubling of vibrations—
the material and the thought world. How does it affect
the circuit in daily work ? When examining patients it is
of little importance. If you think of Mrs. B. and Miss A. as
individuals any thought-forms you may raise merely adds to
the intesnity of the physical reaction. If you were terribly
anxious about cancer you might make a mistake ; if you simply
ask is this reaction I am taking normal or not and measure, the
overlying unconscious thought does not matter. When you
set yourself a test, or try to perform in public, thought may
be a nuisance. This reaction work needs quiet peace of mind.

It is of interest to note that thought-waves can cross a
considerable space, that thought of the whole includes details
unknown to thinker or operator, as when P.R.'s are taken.
Those who are unconscious of telepathy naturally do not
believe in it, but this does not mean it does not exist. We are
all limited in some direction or another ; to most of us is
given but glimpses of a very limited cosmos. However, the
view is expanding for many of us. As the world progresses
the power of thought will be increasingly recognised. Unless
the thought of peace becomes effective in the world in our
time our civilisation goes. Civilisations have gone before
for various reasons. We can save ours by thinking sane,
healthy, generous thoughts about others. Greed, suspicion
and fear will ruin the world financially and spoil our health.

CHAPTER XXII

THE FUTURE

BEFORE any discovery can be made by experiment it must be conceived in the mind unless it occurs in an accidental manner while something else is being searched for. Let us first consider where we stand at the present moment of writing. The circuit originated by Abrams is pre-eminently an instrument for studying life, not for physics. This is well illustrated by the following example : My friend, Major H. P. Pakenham Mahon, worked out a connection between some colour films I sent him and the elements. When I tried to check up his findings on my circuit the colours were thrown on to the elements themselves, no alteration in intensity could be observed, but when I tuned to the corresponding elements in the human body and added colour my findings corresponded with Pakenham Mahon's. For instance among other tests a certain blue increased the activity of bismuth in the human body. For purely physical studies physical apparatus is best. I know that modifications of Abrams' apparatus have been used for finding oil and minerals, but the circuit is cumbrous compared to the use of the divining rod by the dowser. The dowser can pick up the kind of life found in water and minerals, and I have no doubt he could tune to psychic forces. The phenomena of the divining rod are on the same lines as my circuit. Dowsers can do so much in the search for minerals it would be absurd to use a cumbrous apparatus for such purposes. The circuit can be used to find faults in metals, a damaged screw can be picked out from a number of good ones, a fault in a bridge or aeroplane could be found, but a dowser could certainly do the same with a little practice much more rapidly. The future of the Abrams' circuit then lies in the study of life, not physics. We must retain the life-forces of operator and subject. Can the circuit be improved ? I have no doubt it can be made more active by different valves. The tuning in ohms must be retained on account of the correspondence between the atomic and molecular numbers and ohm tuning. Arrangement of rheostats in series must be retained because of the arrangement of the auric rings in series. Higher ohmage may be an advantage to correspond with shorter wave-lengths in the aura. A study of the numbers obtained in the aura and body-tuning of various life-forms is desirable ; they certainly must have a definite meaning which is at present hidden from us. I could hazard a guess at some of them now, but proof would be wanting. The work done so far is a mere fringe of what can be done in the future. The aura needs further work and elucidation. This is what one might call higher vital physics, but physics on a different plane. There is always matter, but matter in a different state of division and activity. The materialist is a man who cannot grasp the idea of one kind of matter ensouling a more closely arranged form of matter. His ideas range purely on the physical plane. Mind and emotion to him are epiphenomena, something he imagines he can explain by increased complexity in the arrangement of proteons and electrons. This idea will die out as will the idea that mind and spirit are phenomena of a totally different kind of physics. I do not suggest I have touched Spirit in the sense that I have demonstrated it ; it is not manifest at present, merely deducible as a needed explanation for pheno- mena. Jung, among other psychologists, recognises this. Maeterlinck finds it necessary to imagine a race over soul to explain the action of termites and other insects. I have shown that the advent of a fresh kind of consciousness goes with an extra ring in the aura and that vibrations can be tuned to in the position in the aura which corresponds to things seen by clairvoyants as mental images. Elaboration and proof of this latter observation is needed in the future. Atomic changes certainly take place in the supposed mental aura in mental disease ; this has to be followed up in a number of cases and the results tabulated as I have done in work on the physical body. Further psychological experiments are needed on the result of certain kinds of thought across space. How does one person affect another ? How do people affect themselves in thought ? I have described some results in the book. Abrams put up the framework of the building we are erecting, his followers have added the bricks ; when eager youths come along with modern physiology and pathology at their fingers'-ends they will raise a building scarcely recog- nisable by the founder. But it will be based on certain principles which form part of natural law. Life means movement, perfect form means rhythmic balance. Life must be measured by life. Let our successors remember that all men's bodies are built up by atoms, and that it is life-forces which maintain their normal rhythm. There is endless work of all kinds to be done, and in the future I hope another link in the chain may soon be added by a demonstration of consciousness after bodily death. A series of experiments are needed on self-induced, hypnotic and mediumistic trance. How ao these differ ? Does the latter consistently show traces of other world-consciousness ? Do thought-forms as described in the chapter show traces of their author ? The powers of the human psyche are so marvellous that we have to carefully analyse and explore them before we allow explanations to be due to discarnate entities. Any experiments which would tend to prove survival of personality would be of first-rate importance. Some may think such evidence unnecessary, that they have sufficient already, others would not believe it anyhow, not desiring survival or being pessimistic as to proof or regarding the world of mind or spirit as something totally different. There is a large class of people who are not satisfied with things as they are and who hunger for further proof. In any case the investigation I suggest would give us knowledge of value. It would necessitate team work, patience and experience, and must be carried out under careful test conditions by people with balanced minds and nervous systems and a sole desire for knowledge and service. There is also the question of where the separated rings of the aura go during trance or sleep. Can these be demonstrated ? Any of these inquiries may involve risks and need to be carried out with due precautions. We are drawing near the end of the extreme materialistic period of thought—it was an essential part of evolution ; so long as man had mainly vertical vision he could not learn much of the horizontal horizon. Authority checked exploration and research. Man had to learn for himself to stand on his own feet. The lesson of walking alone has hardly been learnt ; it has resulted in a hell of a mess. However, we have learnt, or are learning, that something else is needed. Science alone gives greater power to those who lack sense and a feeling of brotherhood Every day the outlook of science broadens, we are learning that knowledge must include more than physics and chemistry, biochemistry will be more interesting when life-forces themselves are studied, and they are most easily studied in the aura. The astronomer sees in the phenomena of the universe the workings of mind. Sir Oliver Lodge believes there is life in the ether. I have been unable to find any force reduplicating on two rheostats coming from the sun or from the atmosphere to corroborate this theory ; early experiments suggested that this occurred but these reduplications proved later to have been caused by our own bodies. This does not mean that there is not life in the ether ; merely that my circuit is not a suitable medium for its demonstration. Speaking generally our bodies do seem to be miniature universes, and therefore we may imagine that the solar system is just an atom implanted in a sea of life, but this is as far as my method of investigation goes ; is just so much poetry, probably true but not demonstrated. Astronomers must find their own method for recognising universal life outside earth life. It will probably include some reduplicating apparatus. It is certain that the universe is built up in a series of reduplications from the infinitely great to the infinitely little ; all forms are built up in similar lines with similar forces in them, and that if we are packed with biomorphs the same arrangement exists throughout. Others may be more successful than myself in clearer skies than London, but the probability is that the human force circuit is not the best apparatus for the job. If life-forces exist in the ether they may be of immensely shorter wave-length or merely comparable to the biomorph found in minerals. There is urgent need for workers who will follow up trails more important than the study of unbalanced bodies which must be my main care and work. I can see no limit to what may be done in the future except the exhaustion of life-forces in one form. To this one must add that the harmonious rhythm of bodily life is dependent on harmony of the psyche. We must be able to see and feel that all our troubles and strivings are not a purposeless maze. I cannot develop this here, but I believe myself that these lives which some of us find so hard and sad and puzzling, and sometimes so joyous and glorious, are but one of a string of such experiences, each one a step in evolution. Nothing is wasted, everything is used in Nature ; this is well expressed by Rudyard Kipling :—

" They will come back, come back again as long as the red earth rolls ;
   He never wasted a leaf or a tree, do you think He would squander
      Souls ? "

Yes ! I think incarnation gives an explanation of many of our difficulties, and is truly evolutionary and is the further extension of the Chain of Life.

INDEX.

Abrams' circuit, 10
— discoveries, 6
— idea of wave effects, 197
— " New Conceptions," 9
— task, 8
Acidity, Effect of glands on, 60
Alcohol, 179
Alkalinity, Effect of glands on, 60
Aluminium poisoning, 183
Asthma, 124
Atomic table, Human, 28
— —, proofs of, 121

Bach, Dr. Edward, 194
Bach's bacillus, 123
Baines, A. E., xi, 5
Balance changes, 44
—, Human, 41
Biomorphs, 84
Birthmark frequencies, 43
Blood-pressure, Effects of glands on, 59
Body compounds, H.I.F., 154
Boyd, Dr. W., 55, 199
Buckingham, Mr. H., Clairvoyance, 92

Cancer, Biomorphs, change in, 163
—, Drugs in, 167, 171
—, Endocrines in, 158
—, Effects of sex life, 178
—, Galvanometer in, 162
—, Gland treatment, 174
—, Guanidin in, 158
—, Macdonagh on, 156
—, Nature of, 155
—, Psychology, 176
—, Polarities in, 160
— results, 177
— virus, 156, 167
Capper, 10
Chronic infections, 123
Circuit, Author's, Fig. i, 12
—, —, Fig. ii, 13
Clairvoyance, 93
Close tuning, Necessity for, 130, 198
Colloids, Balanced, 42
Colour and cancer, 193
— and brain centre, 185

Colour, effect by colour through eyes, 191
—, Lord Clifford, 193
Contraception, 74

Dielectric oil, Use of, xi, 121
Dieting, 179
Dilutions, Nature of High, 32
Dispersers, 121
—, Use in cancer, 172
Dosage, 122
Dowsers, 210

Earthing, Effect of, 16
Education, Faulty, 137
Electrons, Tuning to, 33
Elements, Reactions of, 30
Elimination, Importance of, 131
Endocrines, Tuning, 49
Englund's discovery of body-wave, 5, 199
Entropy, 136
Episternal notch centre, 97, 194
Ether, Life forces in, 213

Fear, Effects of, 139
Function, Importance of, 135

Ghosts, 94
Glands, Emotions and, 63
—, Mental effects of, 80
—, Organisms, effect on, 117
—, Sex gland regulators, 79
Gye and Purdy, 156

Hardin, Dr. M. C., on sex centre, 69
Heart centre, 97
Hessey, Dr. Dodson, xii, 191
Highest intensity frequency, Nature of, 57
Hodgson, Dr. G., as clairvoyant, 194
Homœopathy, Principles of, 139

Inflammation, 119, 120
Internal Secretions, 51
— —, Method of study, 53
— —, Polarities, 56
— —, Recognition of, 54

Kilner, Dr. J., 91
Koch, Dr. W. F., 22, 156

Lefroy, Col. H. P., 18, 84
Locality tuning, 47

Macdonagh, Dr., 156, 160
MacRoberts, Dr. W. J., 59, 201
—, On thought forms, 202
Magnetic fields of earth, 16
Masturbation, 61, 74
Medorrhinum, conditions, 115

Normality index, 42, 47
Nosodes, H.I.F., 154

Ohm and atomic number, 20
—, Clinical proof, 121
Organisms and drugs, 143
— and H.I.F., 153
Organs, Tuning, 47
Oscilloclast, 196
— wave-length, 199
Oxygenation, Effects of glands on, 61

Pakenham Mahon, Major Hales, 210
Parasites, Treatment for, 134
Petrie, Dr. Martha, 29, 197
Polarity of compounds, 37
— of elements, 35
— of emotions, 36

Polarity reversed, 39, 41
— of sexes, 35, 36
Polarization, Mental, 37
Projection, Phenomena, 95

Recognition frequencies, 43
— of sex before birth, 45
Richards, Gerald, Valve set, 14

Screening, 17
Sex balance, 69
— centre in brain, 50, 69
— glands, 66
—, Knowledge of, 73
— production, 71, 73
Sexual intercourse, Exchange of
    secretions, 74
Silvester, Dr. Temple, Gland effects
    on lunatics, 61
—, Neon lamp, 96
Sympathetic, Effect of glands on, 58

Tartaric acids, 38, 39
Taylor Jones, Dr., 199, 200
Thought-forms, 201
—, No aura, 97
—, Experiments, 204, 207

Vannier, Dr. L., 130
Vegetarianism, 181

Wright, Dudley d'A., 24